70s H[illegible]

The Chord Songbook

Wise Publications
London/New York/Paris/Sydney/Copenhagen/Madrid/Tokyo

Exclusive Distributors:

Music Sales Limited
8/9 Frith Street,
London W1D 3JB, England.
Music Sales Pty Limited
120 Rothschild Avenue,
Rosebery, NSW 2018, Australia.

Order No. AM967857
ISBN 0-7119-8532-4

Compiled by Nick Crispin
Music arranged by Rob Smith
Music engraved by The Pitts

Cover photograph courtesy of London Features International

Printed in the United Kingdom by
Caligraving Limited, Thetford, Nolfolk.

Relative Tuning

The guitar can be tuned with the aid of pitch pipes or dedicated electronic guitar tuners which are available through your local music dealer. If you do not have a tuning device, you can use relative tuning. Estimate the pitch of the 6th string as near as possible to E or at least a comfortable pitch (not too high, as you might break other strings in tuning up). Then, while checking the various positions on the diagram, place a finger from your left hand on the:

5th fret of the E or 6th string and **tune the open A** (or 5th string) to the note (A)

5th fret of the A or 5th string and **tune the open D** (or 4th string) to the note (D)

5th fret of the D or 4th string and **tune the open G** (or 3rd string) to the note (G)

4th fret of the G or 3rd string and **tune the open B** (or 2nd string) to the note (B)

5th fret of the B or 2nd string and **tune the open E** (or 1st string) to the note (E)

E or 6th | A or 5th | D or 4th | G or 3rd | B or 2nd | E or 1st

Head

Nut

1st Fret

2nd Fret

3rd Fret

4th Fret (B)

5th Fret (A) (D) (G) (E)

Reading Chord Boxes

Chord boxes are diagrams of the guitar neck viewed head upwards, face on as illustrated. The top horizontal line is the nut, unless a higher fret number is indicated, the others are the frets.

The vertical lines are the strings, starting from E (or 6th) on the left to E (or 1st) on the right.

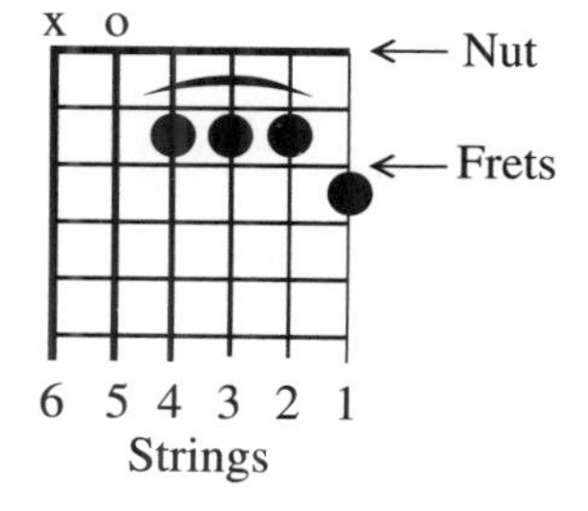

The black dots indicate where to place your fingers.

Strings marked with an O are played open, not fretted.
Strings marked with an X should not be played.

The curved bracket indicates a 'barre' – hold down the strings under the bracket with your first finger, using your other fingers to fret the remaining notes.

All Right Now

Words & Music by
Paul Rodgers & Andy Fraser

A5 D/A Dadd9/11 G5 D E5

fr2

Intro ‖: A5 D/A | A5 | Dadd9/11 D/A | A5 :‖

Verse 1

```
                A5        D/A  A5
There she stood in the    street
 Dadd9/11           D/A          A5
Smiling from her head to her feet.
                          D/A  A5
I said, "Hey now, what is      this now, baby?"
               Dadd9/11      D           A5
Maybe, maybe she's in need of a kiss.
                         D/A  A5
I said, "Hey, what's your name, baby?"
  Dadd9/11        D/A           A5
Maybe we can see things the same.
                           D/A  A5
Now don't you wait or      hesitate,
               Dadd9/11          D            A5
Let's move   before they raise the parking rate.
```

Chorus 1

```
A5          G5                  D          A5
All right   now, baby it's-a all right now.
            G5                  D          A5    | A5    |
All right   now, baby it's-a all right now.
A5            D/A
  Let me tell you now.
```

| A5 | Dadd9/11 D/A | A5 ‖

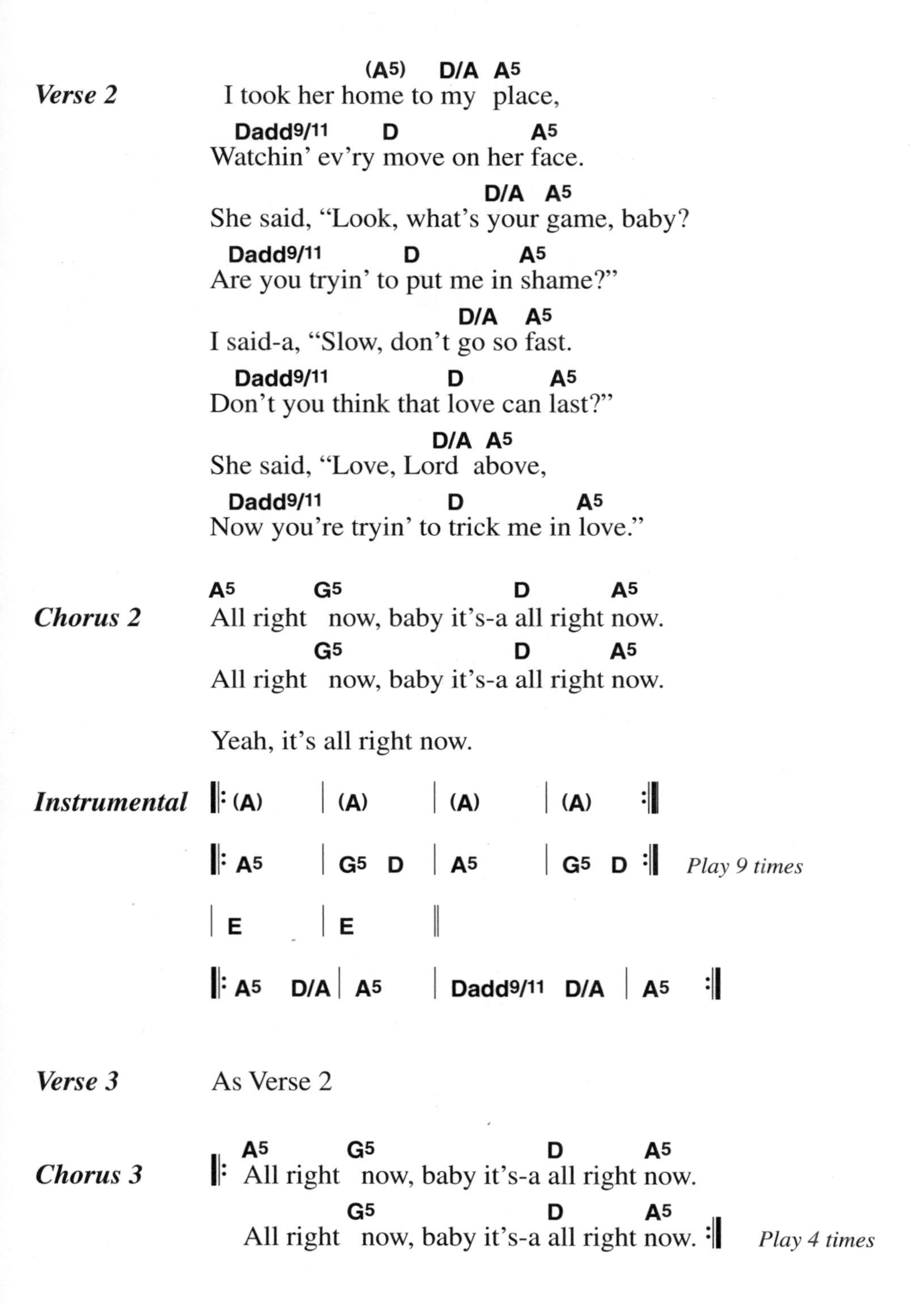

Verse 2
(A5) D/A A5
I took her home to my place,
Dadd9/11 D A5
Watchin' ev'ry move on her face.
D/A A5
She said, "Look, what's your game, baby?
Dadd9/11 D A5
Are you tryin' to put me in shame?"
D/A A5
I said-a, "Slow, don't go so fast.
Dadd9/11 D A5
Don't you think that love can last?"
D/A A5
She said, "Love, Lord above,
Dadd9/11 D A5
Now you're tryin' to trick me in love."
Chorus 2
A5 G5 D A5
All right now, baby it's-a all right now.
G5 D A5
All right now, baby it's-a all right now.
Yeah, it's all right now.
Instrumental
(A) (A) (A) (A)
A5 G5 D A5 G5 D
Play 9 times
E E
A5 D/A A5 Dadd9/11 D/A A5
Verse 3
As Verse 2
Chorus 3
A5 G5 D A5
All right now, baby it's-a all right now.
G5 D A5
All right now, baby it's-a all right now.
Play 4 times

Baker Street

Words & Music by
Gerry Rafferty

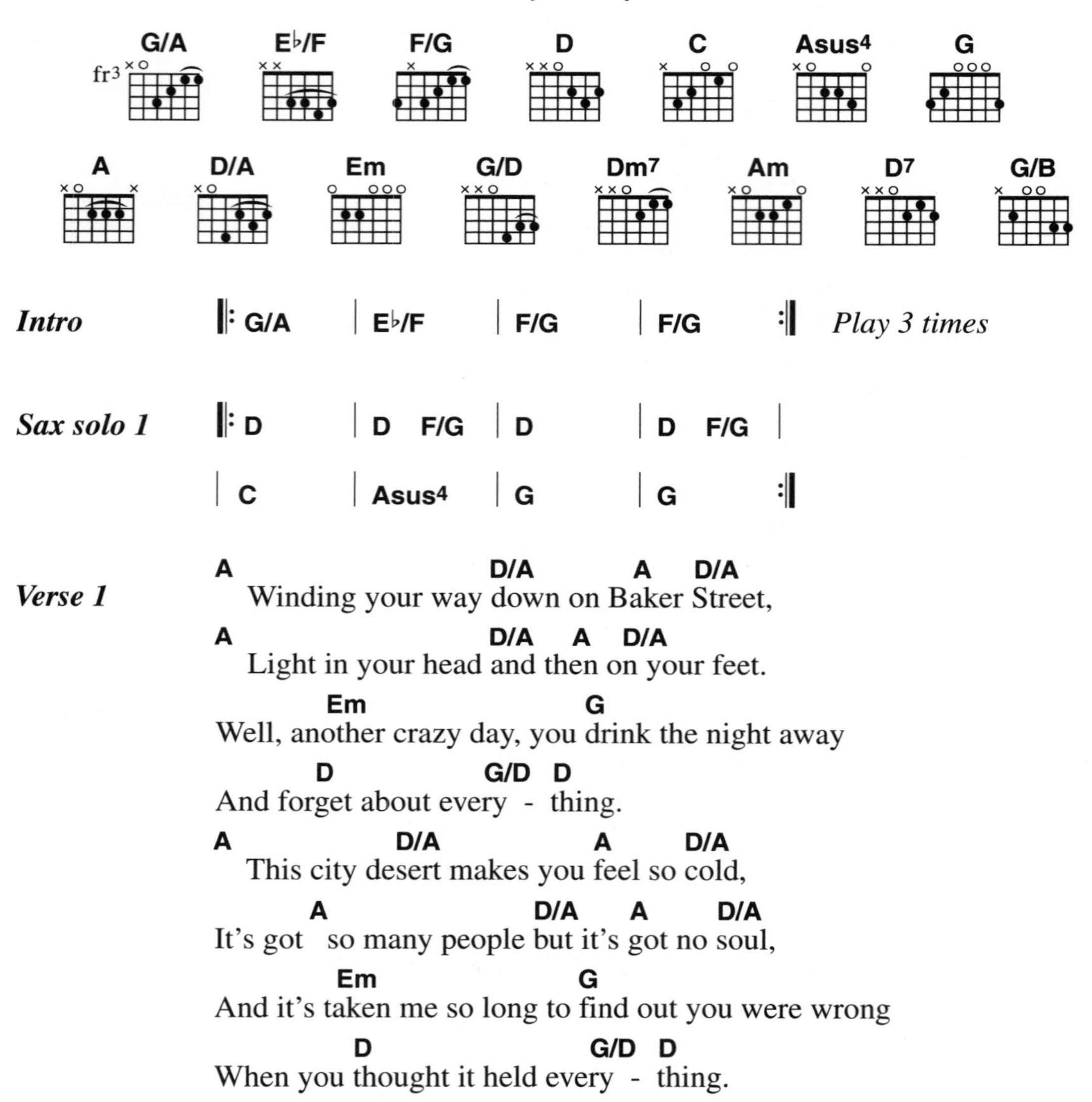

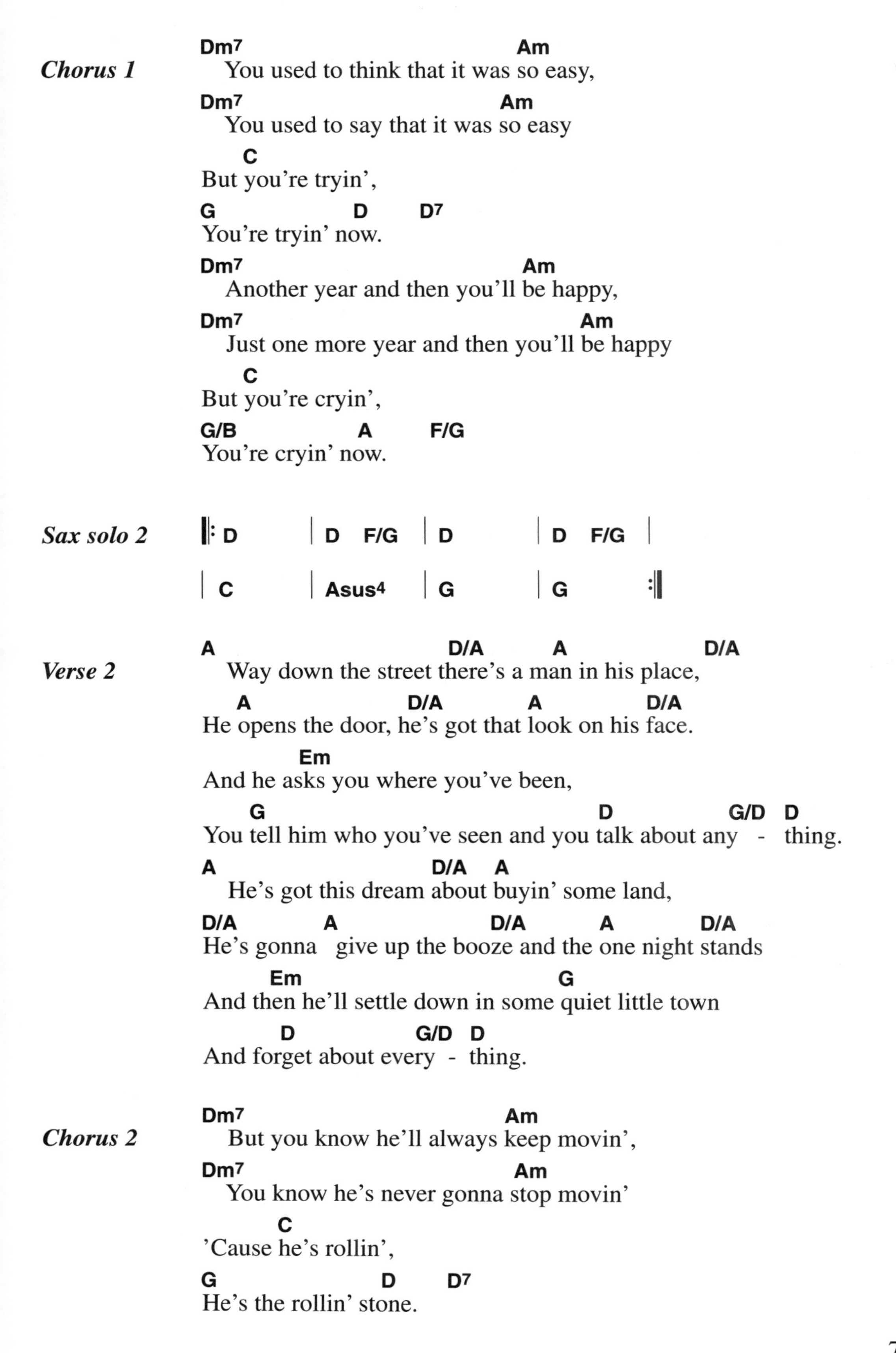

Chorus 1

Dm7 Am
You used to think that it was so easy,

Dm7 Am
You used to say that it was so easy

C
But you're tryin',

G D D7
You're tryin' now.

Dm7 Am
Another year and then you'll be happy,

Dm7 Am
Just one more year and then you'll be happy

C
But you're cryin',

G/B A F/G
You're cryin' now.

Sax solo 2

|: D | D F/G | D | D F/G |

| C | Asus4 | G | G :|

Verse 2

A D/A A D/A
Way down the street there's a man in his place,

A D/A A D/A
He opens the door, he's got that look on his face.

Em
And he asks you where you've been,

G D G/D D
You tell him who you've seen and you talk about any - thing.

A D/A A
He's got this dream about buyin' some land,

D/A A D/A A D/A
He's gonna give up the booze and the one night stands

Em G
And then he'll settle down in some quiet little town

D G/D D
And forget about every - thing.

Chorus 2

Dm7 Am
But you know he'll always keep movin',

Dm7 Am
You know he's never gonna stop movin'

C
'Cause he's rollin',

G D D7
He's the rollin' stone.

cont.

```
Dm7                                 Am
   And when you wake up it's a new morning,
Dm7                            Am
   The sun is shining, it's a new morning,
     C
But you're going,
G/B           A       F/G
You're going home.
```

Sax solo 3

```
||: D       | D   F/G | D       | D   F/G |
|   C       | Asus4   | G       | G       :||
```

Middle

```
||: G/A     | E♭/F    | F/G     | F/G     :||   Play 3 times
```

Guitar solo

```
||: D       | D   F/G | D       | D   F/G |
|   C       | Asus4   | G       | G       :||
```

Outro/ Sax solo 4

```
||: D       | D   F/G | D       | D   F/G |
|   C       | Asus4   | G       | G       :||   Repeat to fade
```

The Boys Are Back In Town

Words & Music by
Phil Lynott

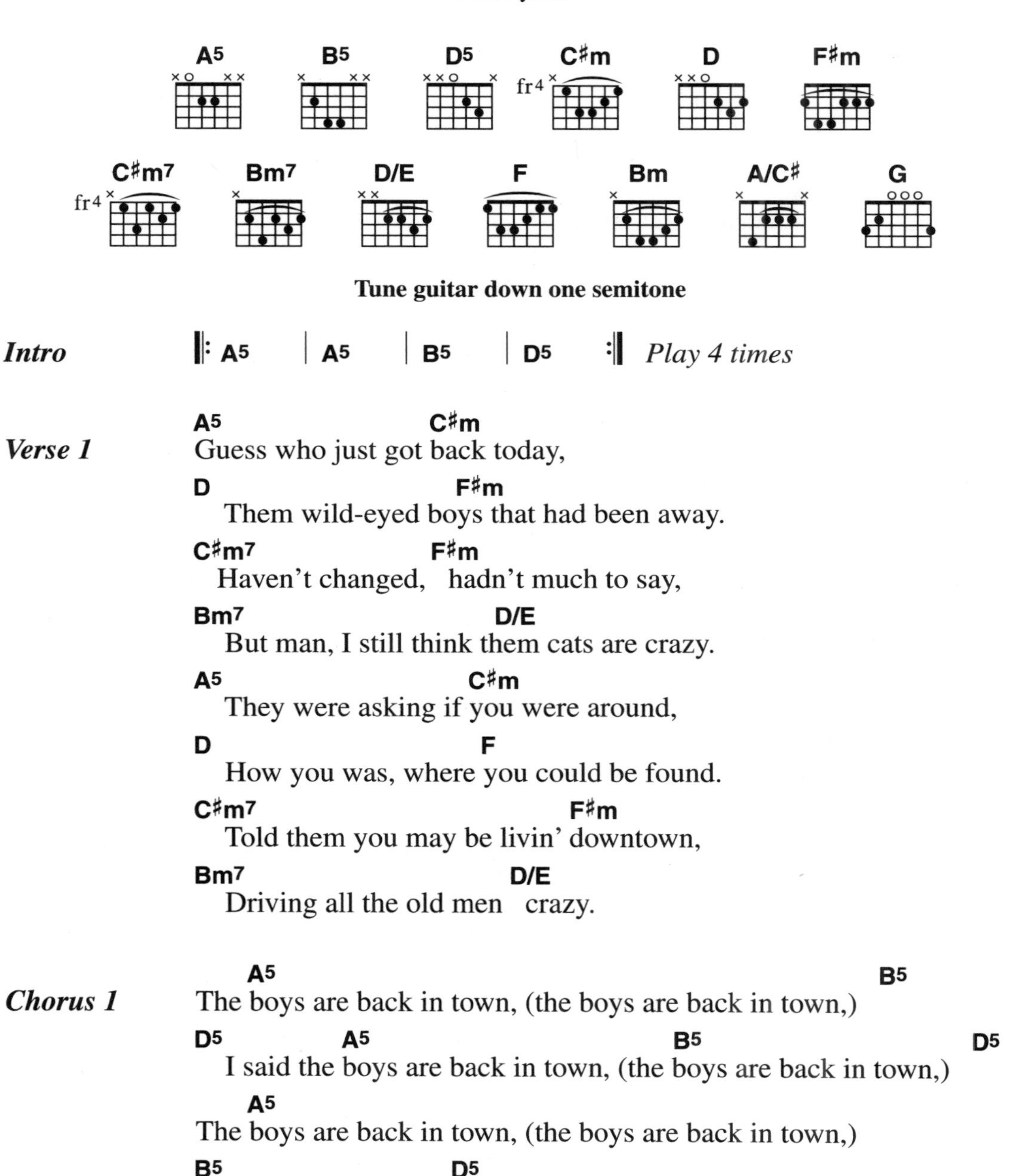

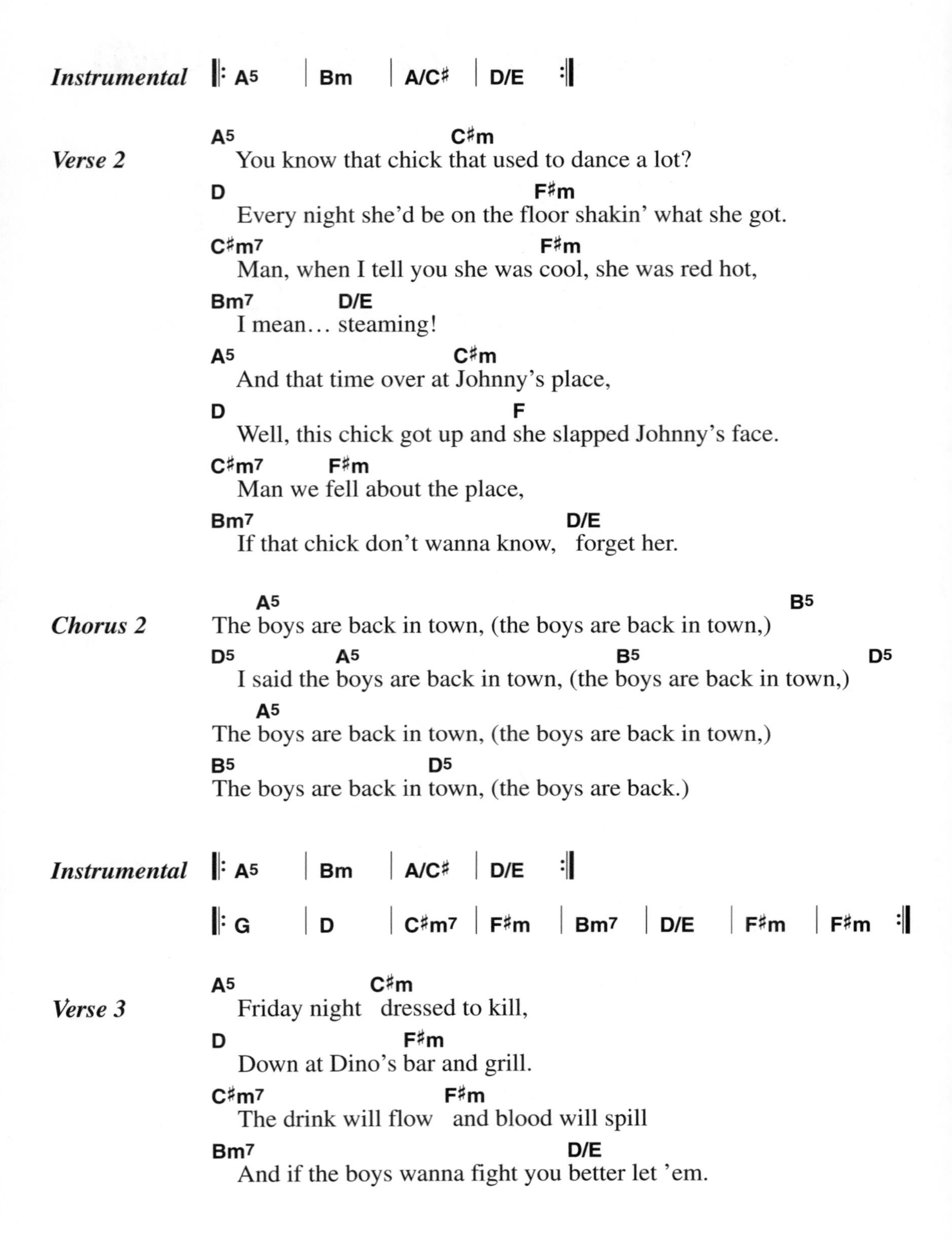

Instrumental |: A5 | Bm | A/C♯ | D/E :|

Verse 2

A5 C♯m
You know that chick that used to dance a lot?

D F♯m
Every night she'd be on the floor shakin' what she got.

C♯m7 F♯m
Man, when I tell you she was cool, she was red hot,

Bm7 D/E
I mean… steaming!

A5 C♯m
And that time over at Johnny's place,

D F
Well, this chick got up and she slapped Johnny's face.

C♯m7 F♯m
Man we fell about the place,

Bm7 D/E
If that chick don't wanna know, forget her.

Chorus 2

A5 B5
The boys are back in town, (the boys are back in town,)

D5 A5 B5 D5
I said the boys are back in town, (the boys are back in town,)

A5
The boys are back in town, (the boys are back in town,)

B5 D5
The boys are back in town, (the boys are back.)

Instrumental |: A5 | Bm | A/C♯ | D/E :|

|: G | D | C♯m7 | F♯m | Bm7 | D/E | F♯m | F♯m :|

Verse 3

A5 C♯m
Friday night dressed to kill,

D F♯m
Down at Dino's bar and grill.

C♯m7 F♯m
The drink will flow and blood will spill

Bm7 D/E
And if the boys wanna fight you better let 'em.

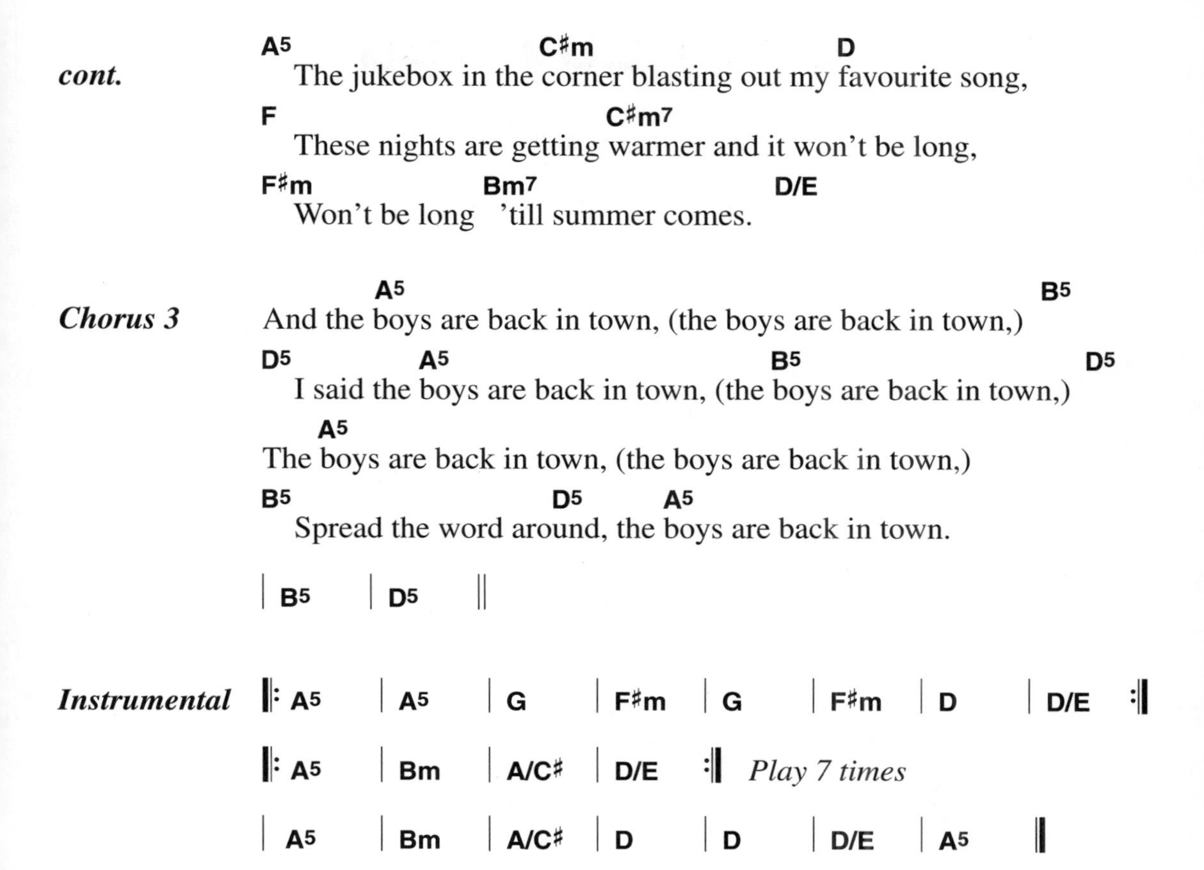

cont.

A5 C♯m D
The jukebox in the corner blasting out my favourite song,

F C♯m7
These nights are getting warmer and it won't be long,

F♯m Bm7 D/E
Won't be long 'till summer comes.

Chorus 3

A5 B5
And the boys are back in town, (the boys are back in town,)

D5 A5 B5 D5
I said the boys are back in town, (the boys are back in town,)

A5
The boys are back in town, (the boys are back in town,)

B5 D5 A5
Spread the word around, the boys are back in town.

| B5 | D5 ||

Instrumental

|: A5 | A5 | G | F♯m | G | F♯m | D | D/E :|

|: A5 | Bm | A/C♯ | D/E :| *Play 7 times*

| A5 | Bm | A/C♯ | D | D | D/E | A5 ||

Coz I Luv You

Words & Music by
Noddy Holder & Jim Lea

Am Dm B♭

Intro | Am | Am ||

Verse 1

```
           Dm
I won't laugh at you, when you boo-hoo-hoo
          Am
Coz I luv you.
          Dm
I can't turn my back on the things you like
          Am
Coz I luv you.
B♭                     Am
I just like the things you do,
B♭                            Am
Don't you change the things you do.
```

Verse 2

```
                 Dm
You get me in a spot, that's all the smile you got
            Am
Then I luv you.
                  Dm
You make me out a clown and you put me down
          Am
I still luv you.
B♭                     Am
I just like the things you do,
B♭                            Am
Don't you change the things you do, yeah.
```

Instrumental |: Dm | Dm | Am | Am :|

|: B♭ | B♭ | Am | Am :|

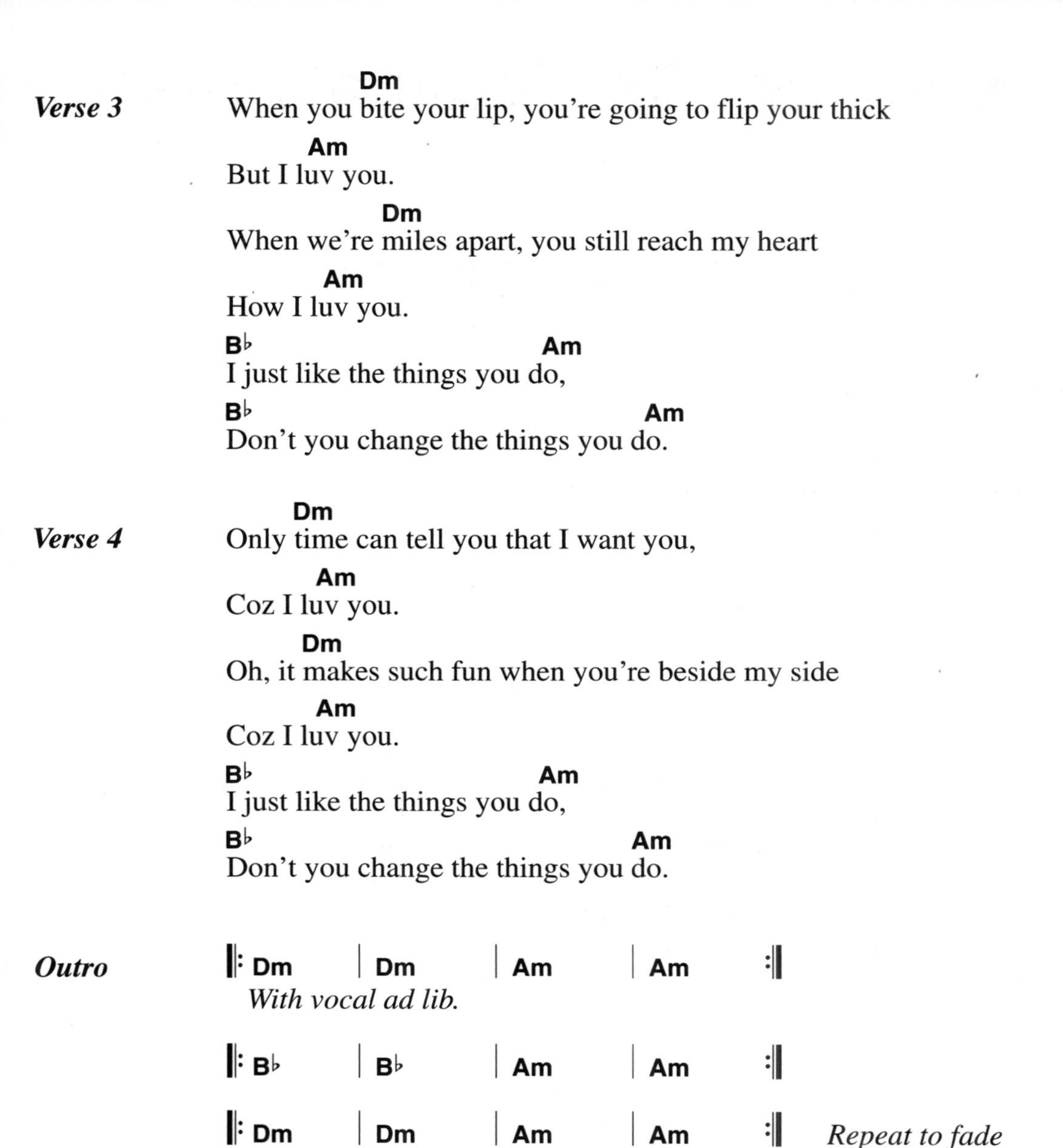

```
                Dm
Verse 3    When you bite your lip, you're going to flip your thick
                 Am
           But I luv you.
                      Dm
           When we're miles apart, you still reach my heart
                   Am
           How I luv you.
           B♭                          Am
           I just like the things you do,
           B♭                                  Am
           Don't you change the things you do.

                  Dm
Verse 4    Only time can tell you that I want you,
                   Am
           Coz I luv you.
                  Dm
           Oh, it makes such fun when you're beside my side
                   Am
           Coz I luv you.
           B♭                          Am
           I just like the things you do,
           B♭                                 Am
           Don't you change the things you do.

Outro      |: Dm    | Dm    | Am    | Am    :|
             With vocal ad lib.

           |: B♭    | B♭    | Am    | Am    :|

           |: Dm    | Dm    | Am    | Am    :|   Repeat to fade
```

Knockin' On Heaven's Door

Words & Music by
Bob Dylan

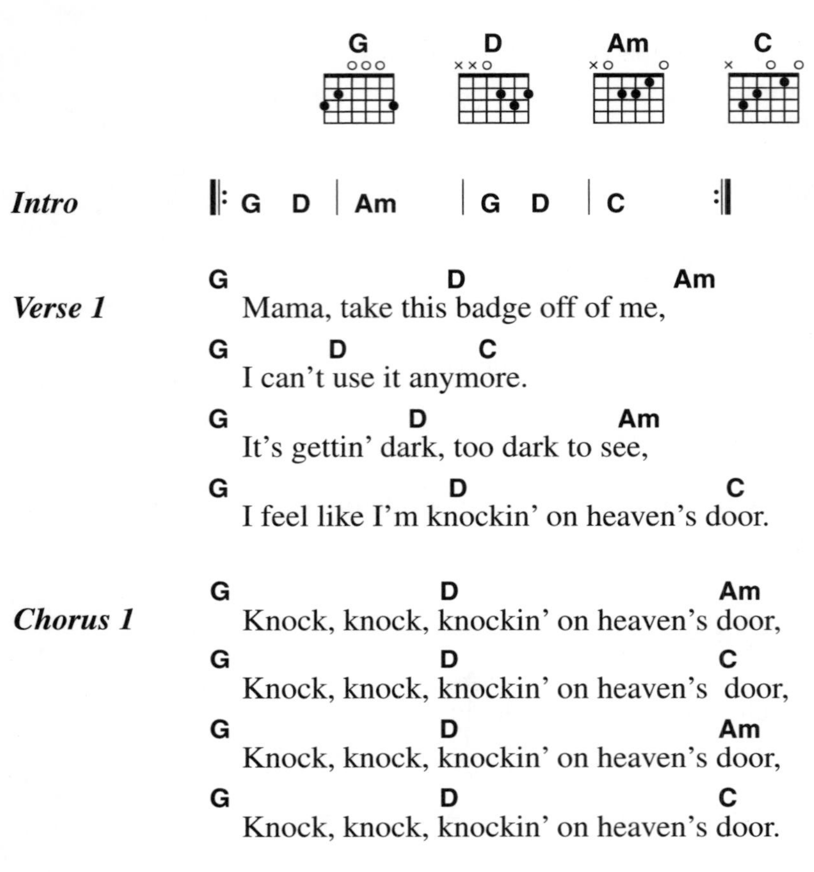

Intro | G D | Am | G D | C :|

Verse 1

G Mama, take this D badge off of me, Am
G I can't D use it C anymore.
G It's gettin' D dark, too dark to Am see,
G I feel like I'm D knockin' on heaven's C door.

Chorus 1

G Knock, knock, D knockin' on heaven's Am door,
G Knock, knock, D knockin' on heaven's C door,
G Knock, knock, D knockin' on heaven's Am door,
G Knock, knock, D knockin' on heaven's C door.

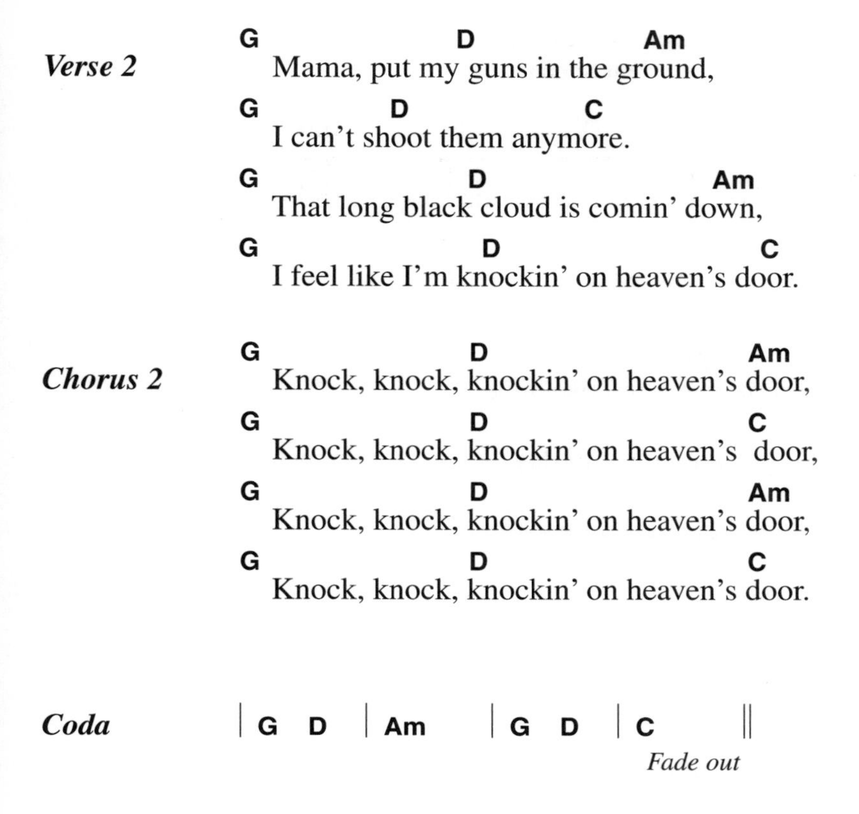

Verse 2

G D Am
Mama, put my guns in the ground,
G D C
I can't shoot them anymore.
G D Am
That long black cloud is comin' down,
G D C
I feel like I'm knockin' on heaven's door.

Chorus 2

G D Am
Knock, knock, knockin' on heaven's door,
G D C
Knock, knock, knockin' on heaven's door,
G D Am
Knock, knock, knockin' on heaven's door,
G D C
Knock, knock, knockin' on heaven's door.

Coda

| G D | Am | G D | C ||

Fade out

Mother And Child Reunion

Words & Music by
Paul Simon

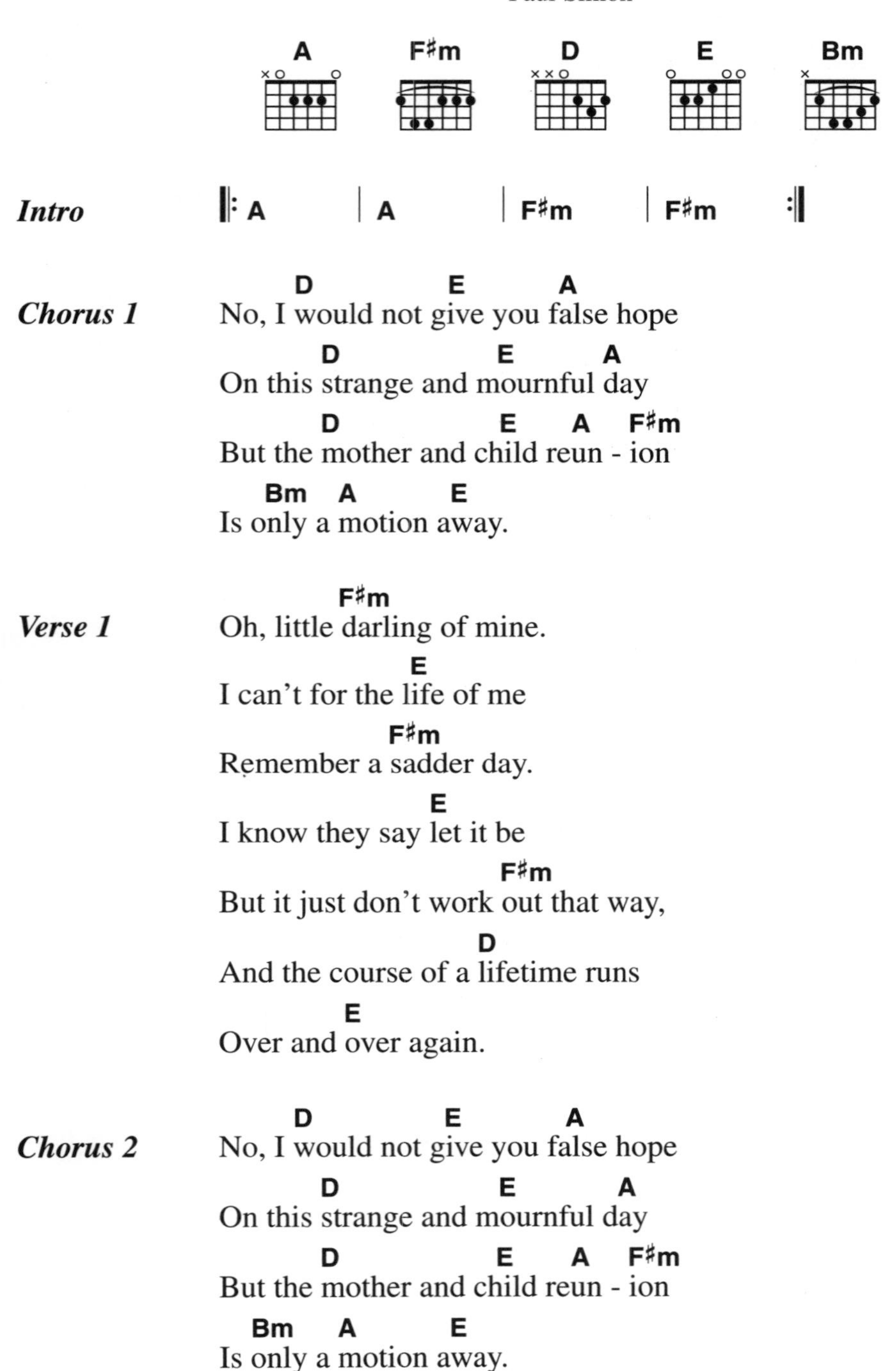

Intro

𝄆 A | A | F♯m | F♯m 𝄇

Chorus 1

```
     D            E        A
No, I would not give you false hope
          D             E       A
On this strange and mournful day
          D             E     A   F♯m
But the mother and child reun - ion
   Bm   A       E
Is only a motion away.
```

Verse 1

```
             F♯m
Oh, little darling of mine.
                 E
I can't for the life of me
                F♯m
Remember a sadder day.
                   E
I know they say let it be
                          F♯m
But it just don't work out that way,
                         D
And the course of a lifetime runs
              E
Over and over again.
```

Chorus 2

```
     D            E        A
No, I would not give you false hope
          D             E       A
On this strange and mournful day
          D             E     A   F♯m
But the mother and child reun - ion
   Bm   A       E
Is only a motion away.
```

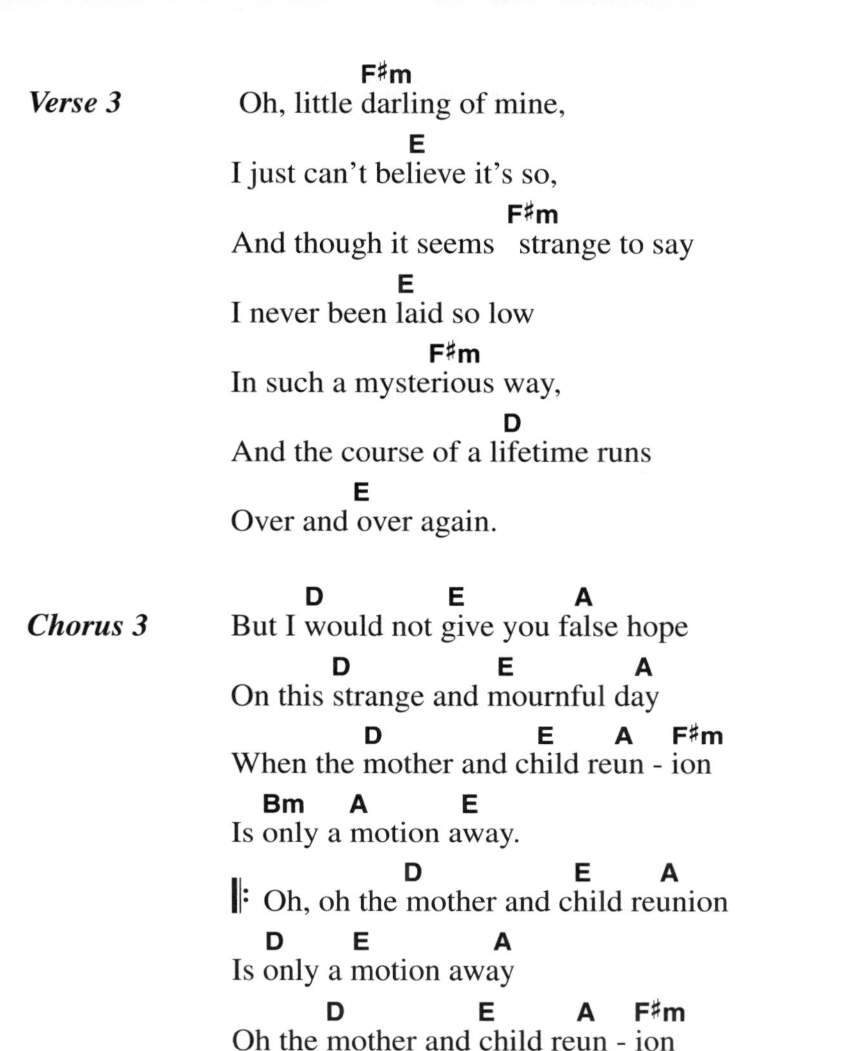

```
                    F♯m
Verse 3       Oh, little darling of mine,
                        E
              I just can't believe it's so,
                                F♯m
              And though it seems  strange to say
                        E
              I never been laid so low
                           F♯m
              In such a mysterious way,
                                     D
              And the course of a lifetime runs
                     E
              Over and over again.

                  D          E          A
Chorus 3      But I would not give you false hope
                     D            E          A
              On this strange and mournful day
                        D              E    A   F♯m
              When the mother and child reun - ion
                 Bm   A      E
              Is only a motion away.
                          D             E     A
              𝄆 Oh, oh the mother and child reunion
                 D    E        A
              Is only a motion away
                      D           E     A   F♯m
              Oh the mother and child reun - ion
                 Bm   A       E
              Is only a moment away.  𝄇   Repeat to fade
```

Mull Of Kintyre

Words & Music by
Paul McCartney & Denny Laine

A D E G

Intro | A | A | A | A ‖

```
Chorus 1      A
              Mull of Kintyre,
                  D                     A
              Oh, mist rolling in from the sea.
                         D
              My desire is always to be here,
                  A
              Oh, Mull of Kintyre.
```

Link 1 | A | A ‖

```
Verse 1       A
              Far have I travelled and much have I seen,
              D                              A
              Dark distant mountains with valleys of green.

              Past painted deserts, the sunset's on fire
                      D                   E          A
              As he carries me home to the Mull of Kintyre.
```

Chorus 2 As Chorus 1

Link 2 | A | A | A | A ‖

Instrumental | D | D | G | G |
| D | D | G | G |
| D | D | D | D ‖

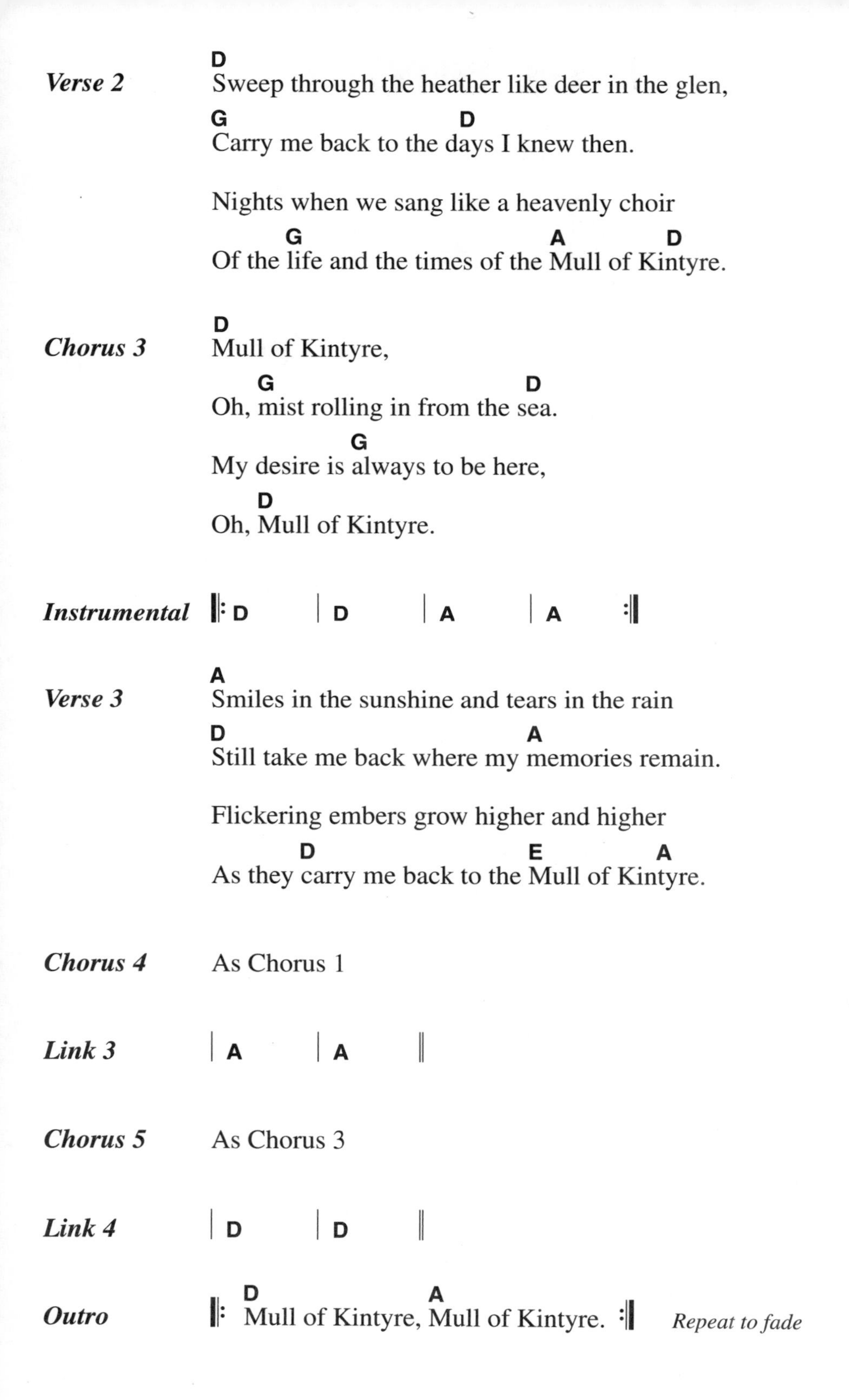
Verse 2
D
Sweep through the heather like deer in the glen,
G D
Carry me back to the days I knew then.
Nights when we sang like a heavenly choir
G A D
Of the life and the times of the Mull of Kintyre.
Chorus 3
D
Mull of Kintyre,
G D
Oh, mist rolling in from the sea.
G
My desire is always to be here,
D
Oh, Mull of Kintyre.
Instrumental
‖: D | D | A | A :‖
Verse 3
A
Smiles in the sunshine and tears in the rain
D A
Still take me back where my memories remain.
Flickering embers grow higher and higher
D E A
As they carry me back to the Mull of Kintyre.
Chorus 4
As Chorus 1
Link 3
| A | A ‖
Chorus 5
As Chorus 3
Link 4
| D | D ‖
Outro
D A
‖: Mull of Kintyre, Mull of Kintyre. :‖
Repeat to fade

Free Bird

Words & Music by
Allen Collins & Ronnie Van Zant

G D/F♯ Em F
C Dsus4 D Dsus2 B♭

Intro

| G | D/F♯ | Em | Em |
| F | C | Dsus4 D | Dsus2 D |
‖: G | D/F♯ | Em | Em | F |
| C | Dsus4 D Dsus2 D | Dsus4 D Dsus2 D :‖ *Play 3 times*

Verse 1

G D/ F♯ Em
If I leave here tomorrow
F C Dsus4 D Dsus2 D
Would you still remember me?______________

| Dsus4 D Dsus2 D |

G D/F♯ Em
For I must be travelling on now
F C Dsus4 D Dsus2 D
'Cos there's too many places I've got to see.____________

| Dsus4 D Dsus2 D |

G D/F♯ Em
And if I stay here with you girl,
F C Dsus4 D Dsus2 D
Things just couldn't be the same.____________

| Dsus4 D Dsus2 D |

G D/F♯ Em
'Cos I'm as free as a bird now,
F C Dsus4 D Dsus2 D
And this bird you cannot change, ____________

Dsus4 D Dsus2 D
Oh.____________

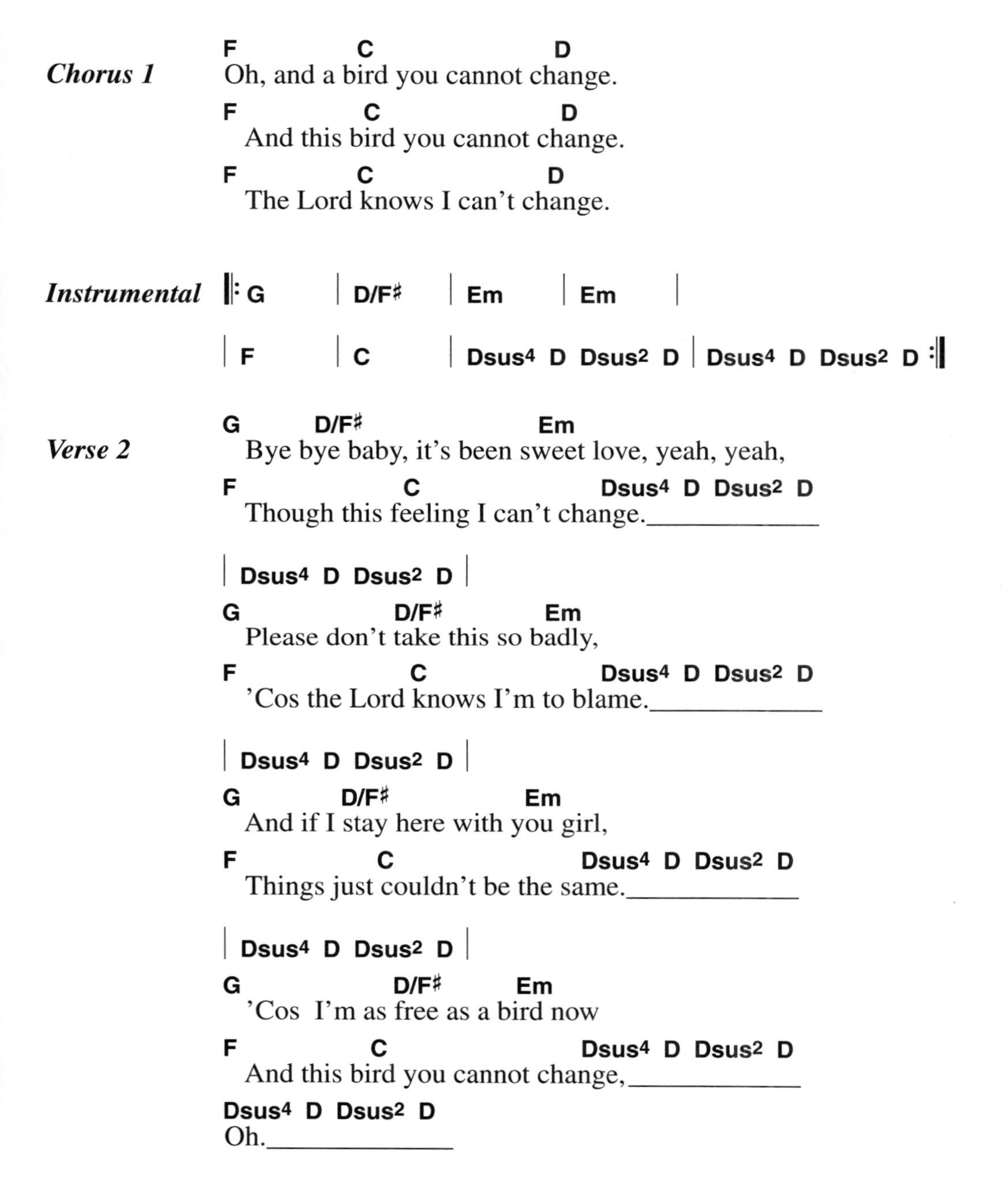

Chorus 1
F C D
Oh, and a bird you cannot change.
F C D
And this bird you cannot change.
F C D
The Lord knows I can't change.
Instrumental
G | D/F♯ | Em | Em |
F | C | Dsus4 D Dsus2 D | Dsus4 D Dsus2 D
Verse 2
G D/F♯ Em
Bye bye baby, it's been sweet love, yeah, yeah,
F C Dsus4 D Dsus2 D
Though this feeling I can't change.
Dsus4 D Dsus2 D
G D/F♯ Em
Please don't take this so badly,
F C Dsus4 D Dsus2 D
'Cos the Lord knows I'm to blame.
Dsus4 D Dsus2 D
G D/F♯ Em
And if I stay here with you girl,
F C Dsus4 D Dsus2 D
Things just couldn't be the same.
Dsus4 D Dsus2 D
G D/F♯ Em
'Cos I'm as free as a bird now
F C Dsus4 D Dsus2 D
And this bird you cannot change,
Dsus4 D Dsus2 D
Oh.

Chorus 2

```
F            C                      D
Oh, and a bird you cannot change.
F             C                     D
  And this bird you cannot change.
F             C                   D
  The Lord knows I can't change.
F        C                D
  Lord, help me, I can't change.
```

Middle

```
G  B♭        C
   Lord, I can't change.
               G   B♭  C
Won't you fly____ freebird, yeah.
```

Gtr Solo

```
|: G     | B♭     | C     | C     :|
```

Repeat to fade

My Sweet Lord

Words & Music by
George Harrison

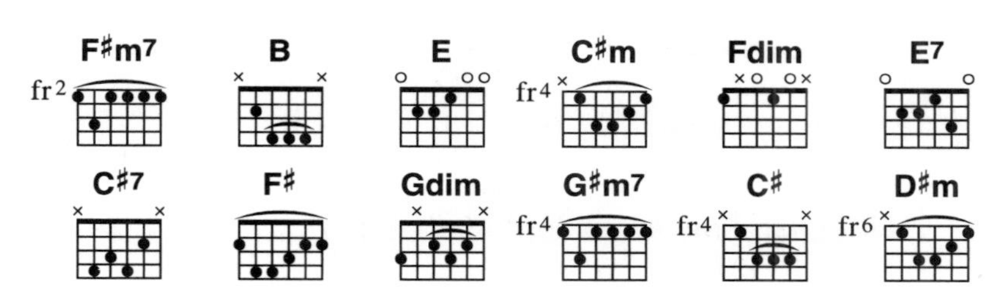

Intro

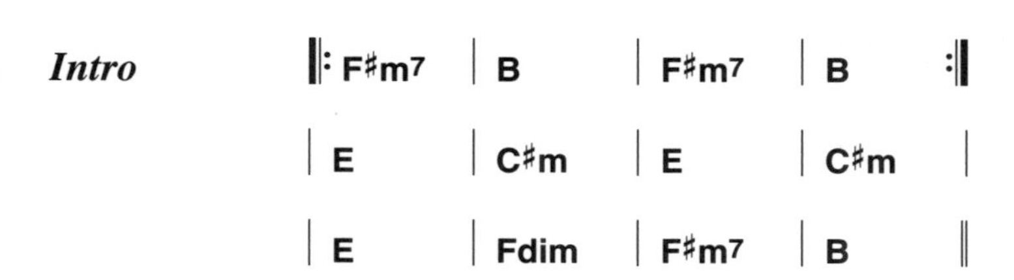

Chorus 1

```
(B)             F♯m7
   My sweet lord,
B              F♯m7
   Mm, my lord,
B              F♯m7
   Mm, my lord.
```

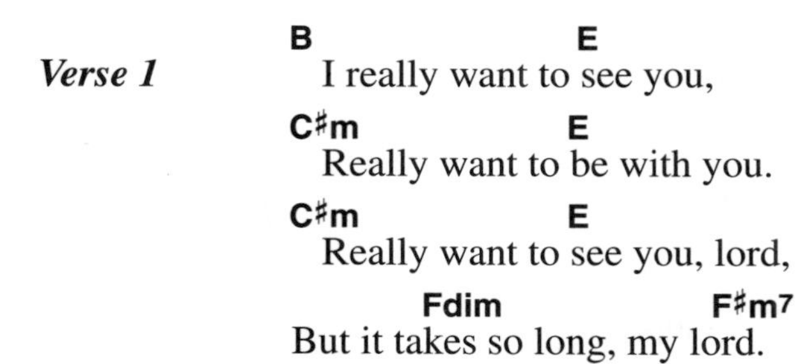

Verse 1

```
B                     E
   I really want to see you,
C♯m                   E
   Really want to be with you.
C♯m                   E
   Really want to see you, lord,
          Fdim                 F♯m7
But it takes so long, my lord.
```

Chorus 2

```
B               F♯m7
   My sweet lord,
B              F♯m7
   Mm, my lord,
B              F♯m7
   Mm, my lord.
```

Verse 2

```
B                 E
  I really want to know you,
C♯m               E
  Really want to go with you.
C♯m               E
  Really want to show you, lord,
         Fdim                  F♯m7
That it won't take long, my lord.
```

Chorus 3

```
       B                  F♯m7      B
(Hallelujah,) my sweet lord, (hallelujah,)
            F♯m7     B
Mm, my lord, (hallelujah,)
             F♯m7    B
My sweet lord, (hallelujah.)
```

Middle

```
                   E
I really want to see you,
                  E7
Really want to see you.
                  C♯7
Really want to see you, lord,
                  F♯
Really want to see you, lord,
         Gdim          G♯m7
But it takes so long, my lord.
```

Chorus 4

```
       C♯                 G♯m7      C♯
(Hallelujah,) my sweet lord, (hallelujah,)
            G♯m7    C♯
Mm, my lord, (hallelujah,)
                G♯m7    C♯
My, my, my lord, (hallelujah.)
```

Verse 3

```
                  F♯               D♯m
I really want to know you, (hallelujah,)
                  F♯                 D♯m
Really want to go with you, (hallelujah.)
                  F♯
Really want to show you, lord,
         Gdim              G♯m7
That it won't take long, my lord.
```

Chorus 5

```
       C♯       G♯m7     C♯
(Hallelujah,) mm, (hallelujah,)
             G♯m7    C♯
My sweet lord, (hallelujah,)
            G♯m7    C♯
My, my lord, (hallelujah.)
```

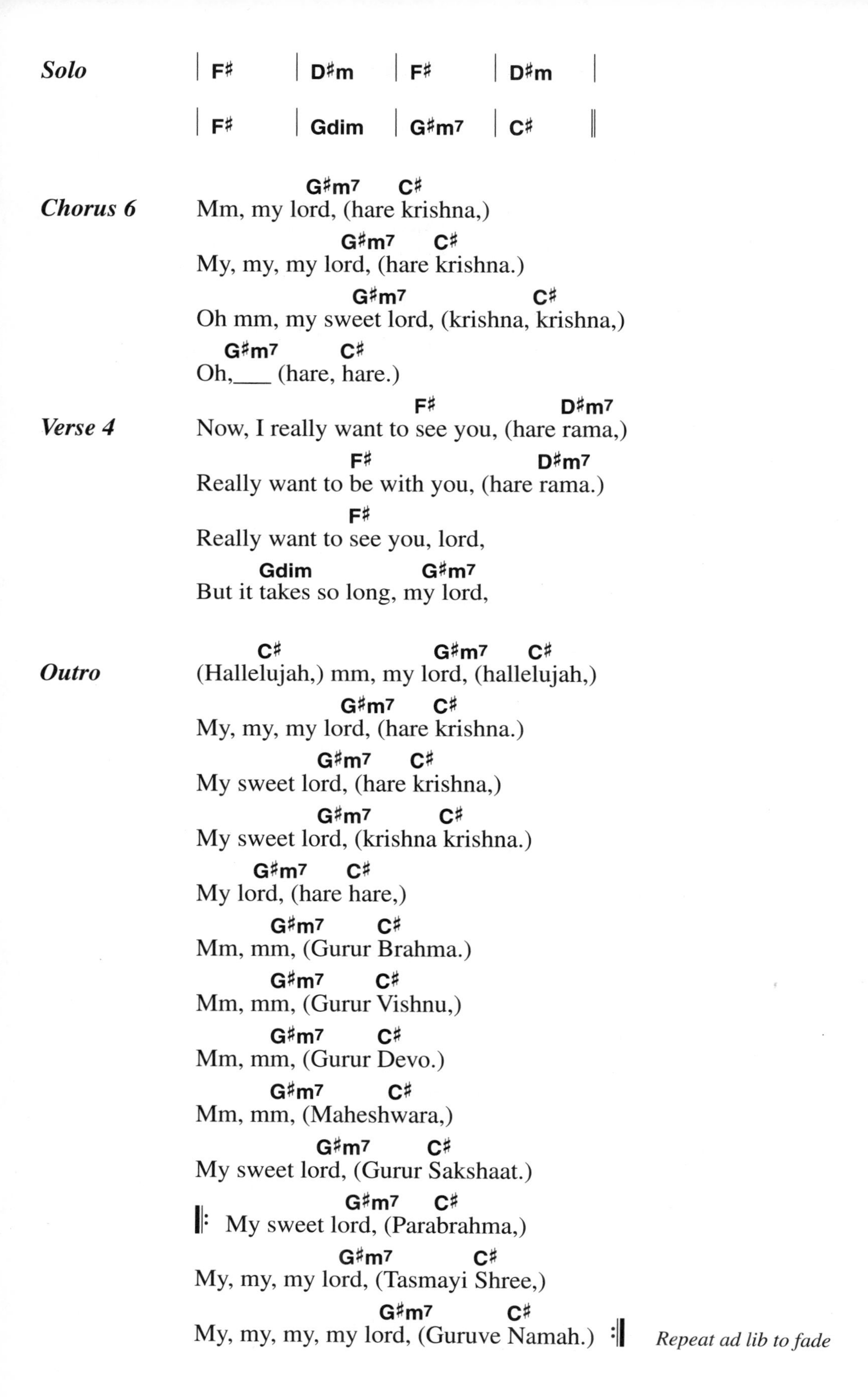

Solo

| F♯ | D♯m | F♯ | D♯m |
| F♯ | Gdim | G♯m7 | C♯ ||

Chorus 6

G♯m7 C♯
Mm, my lord, (hare krishna,)

G♯m7 C♯
My, my, my lord, (hare krishna.)

G♯m7 C♯
Oh mm, my sweet lord, (krishna, krishna,)

G♯m7 C♯
Oh,___ (hare, hare.)

Verse 4

F♯ D♯m7
Now, I really want to see you, (hare rama,)

F♯ D♯m7
Really want to be with you, (hare rama.)

F♯
Really want to see you, lord,

Gdim G♯m7
But it takes so long, my lord,

Outro

C♯ G♯m7 C♯
(Hallelujah,) mm, my lord, (hallelujah,)

G♯m7 C♯
My, my, my lord, (hare krishna.)

G♯m7 C♯
My sweet lord, (hare krishna,)

G♯m7 C♯
My sweet lord, (krishna krishna.)

G♯m7 C♯
My lord, (hare hare,)

G♯m7 C♯
Mm, mm, (Gurur Brahma.)

G♯m7 C♯
Mm, mm, (Gurur Vishnu,)

G♯m7 C♯
Mm, mm, (Gurur Devo.)

G♯m7 C♯
Mm, mm, (Maheshwara,)

G♯m7 C♯
My sweet lord, (Gurur Sakshaat.)

G♯m7 C♯
||: My sweet lord, (Parabrahma,)

G♯m7 C♯
My, my, my lord, (Tasmayi Shree,)

G♯m7 C♯
My, my, my, my lord, (Guruve Namah.) :|| *Repeat ad lib to fade*

Night Fever

Words & Music by
Barry Gibb, Maurice Gibb & Robin Gibb

Intro ‖: C♯m7 | F♯m7 | Emaj7 | F♯m7 :‖

Verse 1

B
Listen to the ground,
A
There is movement all around,
E
There is something goin' down
B
And I can feel it.

On the waves of the air,
C♯m
There is dancin' out there,
E A
If it's somethin' we can share
B
We can steal it.

Pre-chorus 1

G♯m
And that sweet city woman,
A
She moves through the light
G♯m D♯m
Controlling my mind and my soul.
G♯m
When you reach out for me
C♯m G♯
Yeah, and the feelin' is bright.

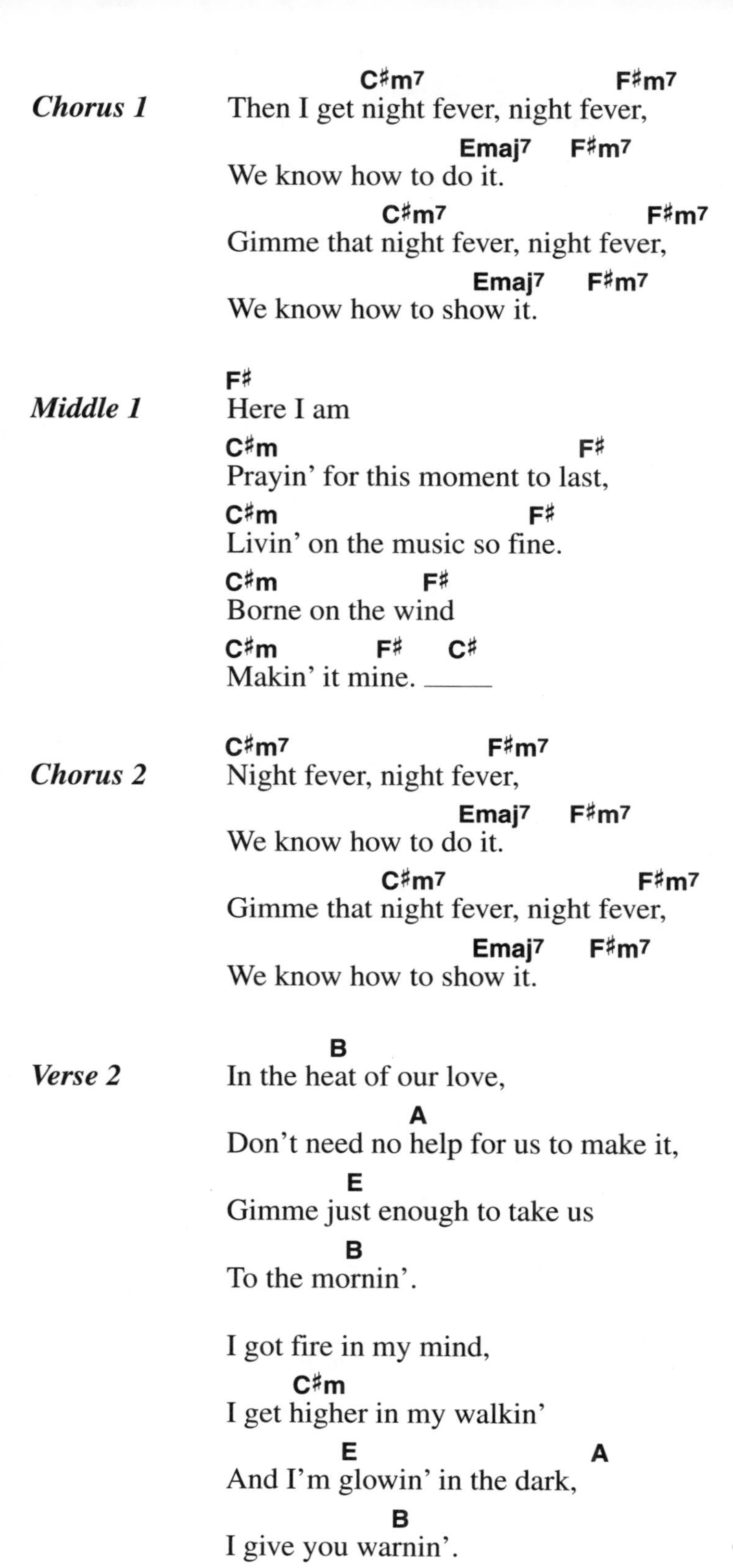

Chorus 1

C♯m7 F♯m7
Then I get night fever, night fever,
Emaj7 F♯m7
We know how to do it.
C♯m7 F♯m7
Gimme that night fever, night fever,
Emaj7 F♯m7
We know how to show it.

Middle 1

F♯
Here I am
C♯m F♯
Prayin' for this moment to last,
C♯m F♯
Livin' on the music so fine.
C♯m F♯
Borne on the wind
C♯m F♯ C♯
Makin' it mine. ____

Chorus 2

C♯m7 F♯m7
Night fever, night fever,
Emaj7 F♯m7
We know how to do it.
C♯m7 F♯m7
Gimme that night fever, night fever,
Emaj7 F♯m7
We know how to show it.

Verse 2

B
In the heat of our love,
A
Don't need no help for us to make it,
E
Gimme just enough to take us
B
To the mornin'.

I got fire in my mind,
C♯m
I get higher in my walkin'
E A
And I'm glowin' in the dark,
B
I give you warnin'.

Pre-chorus 2

And that sweet city woman,

A
She moves through the light

G♯m D♯m
Controlling my mind and my soul.

G♯m
When you reach out for me

C♯m G♯
Yeah, and the feelin' is bright.

Chorus 3

C♯m7 F♯m7
Then I get night fever, night fever,

Emaj7 F♯m7
We know how to do it.

C♯m7 F♯m7
Gimme that night fever, night fever,

Emaj7 F♯m7
We know how to show it.

Middle 2

F♯
Here I am

C♯m F♯
Prayin' for this moment to last,

C♯m F♯
Livin' on the music so fine.

C♯m F♯
Borne on the wind

C♯m F♯ C♯
Makin' it mine. ____

Chorus 4

C♯m7 F♯m7
𝄆 Gimme that night fever, night fever,

Emaj7 F♯m7
We know how to do it.

C♯m7 F♯m7
Just gimme that night fever, night fever,

Emaj7 F♯m7
We know how to show it. 𝄇 *Repeat to fade*

No Woman, No Cry

Words & Music by
Vincent Ford

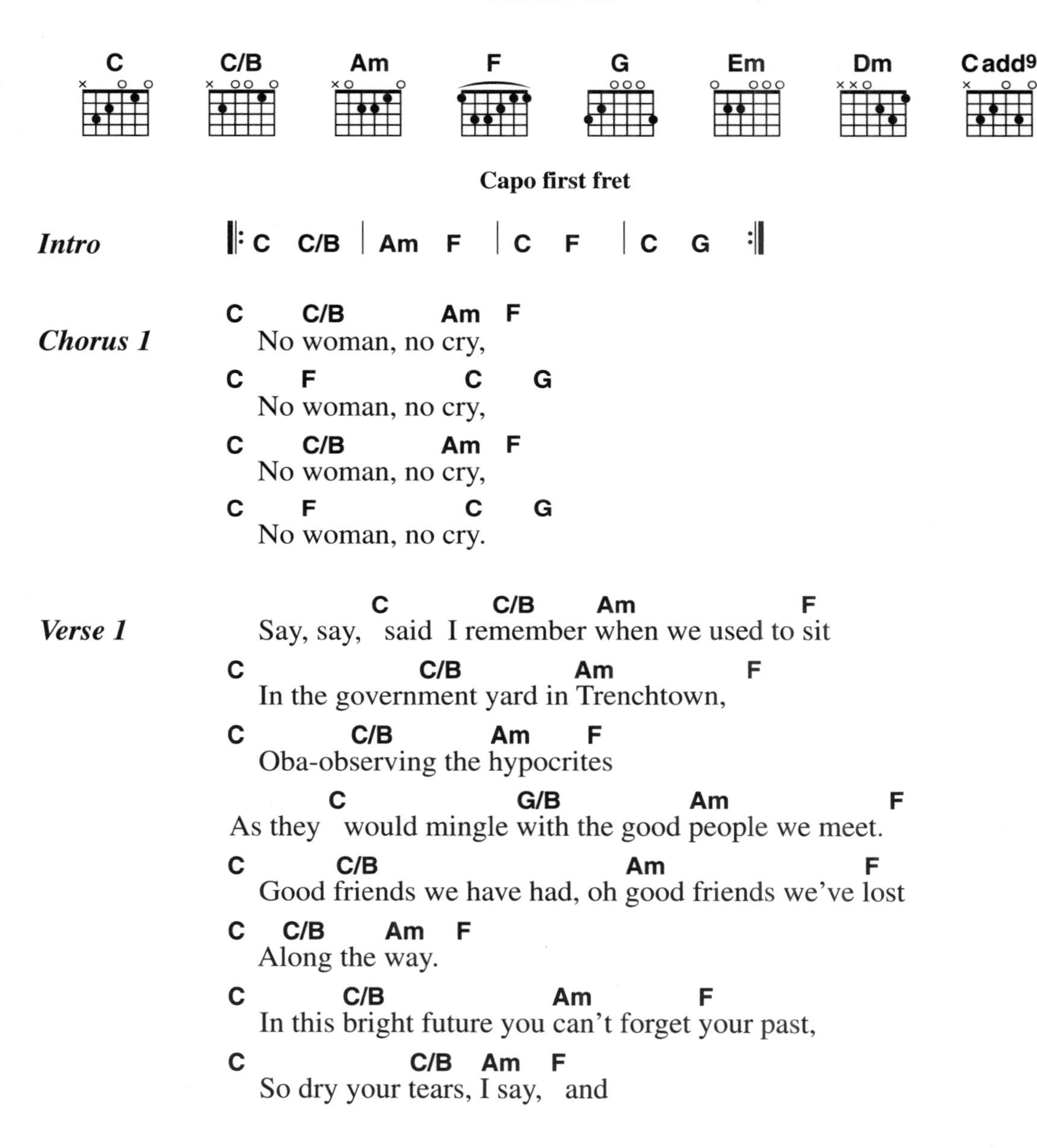

C C/B Am F G Em Dm Cadd9

Capo first fret

Intro ‖: C C/B | Am F | C F | C G :‖

Chorus 1

C C/B Am F
No woman, no cry,
C F C G
No woman, no cry,
C C/B Am F
No woman, no cry,
C F C G
No woman, no cry.

Verse 1

C C/B Am F
Say, say, said I remember when we used to sit
C C/B Am F
In the government yard in Trenchtown,
C C/B Am F
Oba-observing the hypocrites
C G/B Am F
As they would mingle with the good people we meet.
C C/B Am F
Good friends we have had, oh good friends we've lost
C C/B Am F
Along the way.
C C/B Am F
In this bright future you can't forget your past,
C C/B Am F
So dry your tears, I say, and

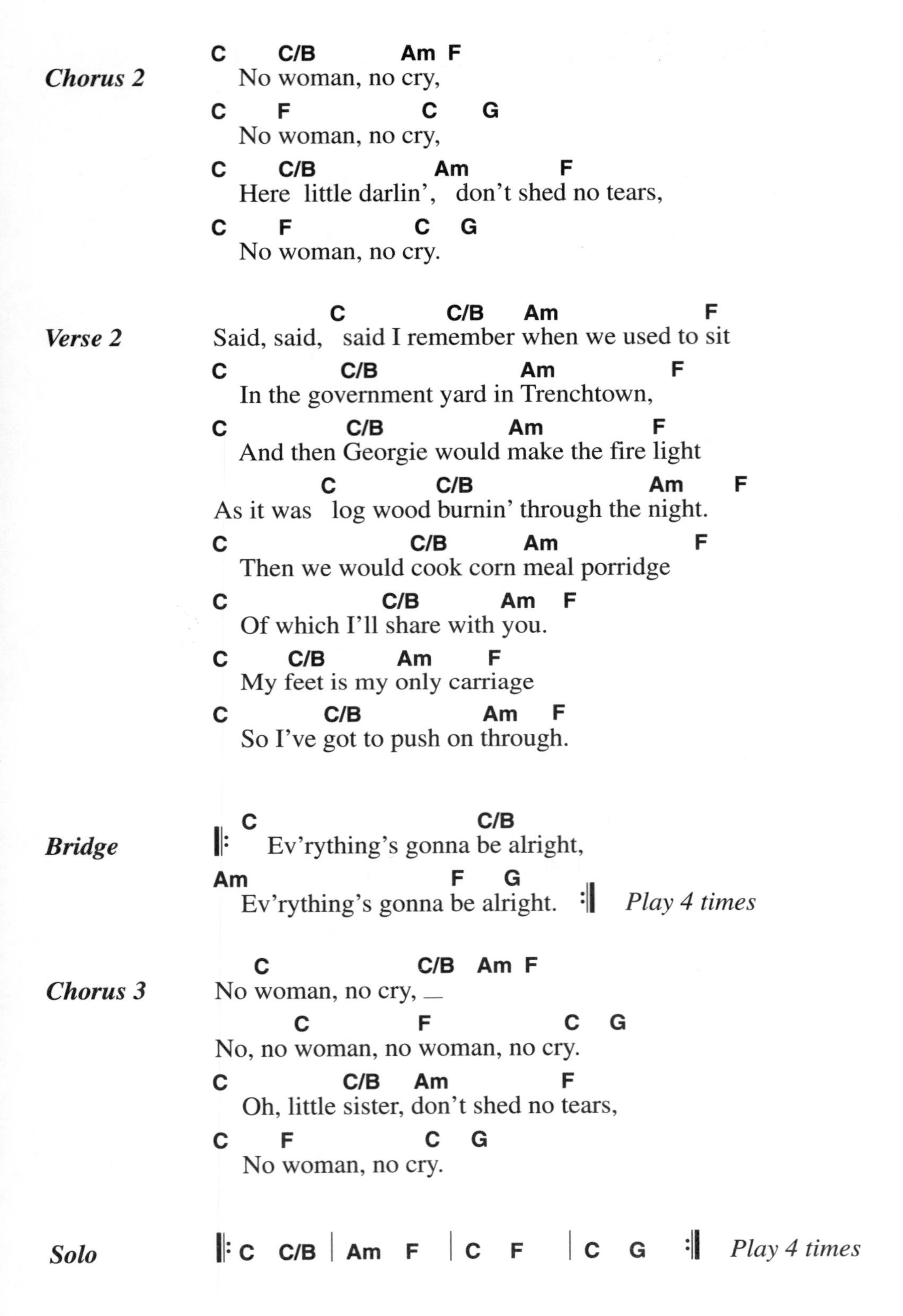

Chorus 2

C C/B Am F
No woman, no cry,
C F C G
No woman, no cry,
C C/B Am F
Here little darlin', don't shed no tears,
C F C G
No woman, no cry.

Verse 2

C C/B Am F
Said, said, said I remember when we used to sit
C C/B Am F
In the government yard in Trenchtown,
C C/B Am F
And then Georgie would make the fire light
C C/B Am F
As it was log wood burnin' through the night.
C C/B Am F
Then we would cook corn meal porridge
C C/B Am F
Of which I'll share with you.
C C/B Am F
My feet is my only carriage
C C/B Am F
So I've got to push on through.

Bridge

C C/B
𝄆 Ev'rything's gonna be alright,
Am F G
Ev'rything's gonna be alright. 𝄇 *Play 4 times*

Chorus 3

C C/B Am F
No woman, no cry, _
C F C G
No, no woman, no woman, no cry.
C C/B Am F
Oh, little sister, don't shed no tears,
C F C G
No woman, no cry.

Solo

𝄆 C C/B | Am F | C F | C G 𝄇 *Play 4 times*

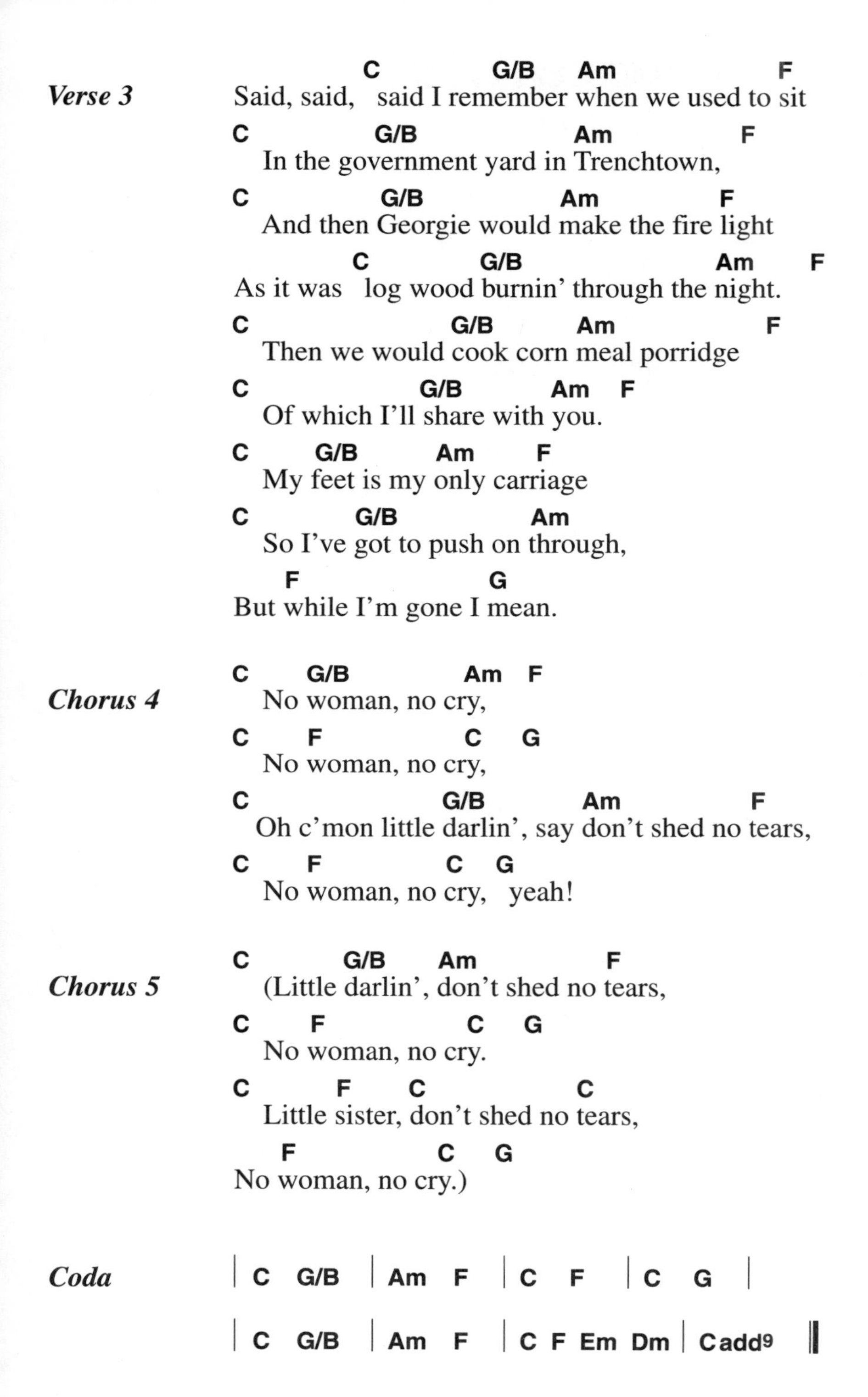

Verse 3

```
                C           G/B     Am           F
Said, said,  said I remember when we used to sit
C           G/B              Am           F
  In the government yard in Trenchtown,
C            G/B            Am           F
  And then Georgie would make the fire light
            C           G/B               Am      F
As it was  log wood burnin' through the night.
C                  G/B       Am                F
  Then we would cook corn meal porridge
C               G/B         Am   F
  Of which I'll share with you.
C       G/B        Am       F
  My feet is my only carriage
C          G/B             Am
  So I've got to push on through,
   F                 G
But while I'm gone I mean.
```

Chorus 4

```
C       G/B         Am   F
  No woman, no cry,
C      F            C    G
  No woman, no cry,
C                      G/B          Am            F
  Oh c'mon little darlin', say don't shed no tears,
C      F            C   G
  No woman, no cry,   yeah!
```

Chorus 5

```
C        G/B     Am           F
  (Little darlin', don't shed no tears,
C      F            C    G
  No woman, no cry.
C        F     C           C
  Little sister, don't shed no tears,
   F            C    G
No woman, no cry.)
```

Coda

```
| C  G/B | Am  F | C  F | C  G |

| C  G/B | Am  F | C F Em Dm | Cadd9 ||
```

Roxanne

Words & Music by
Sting

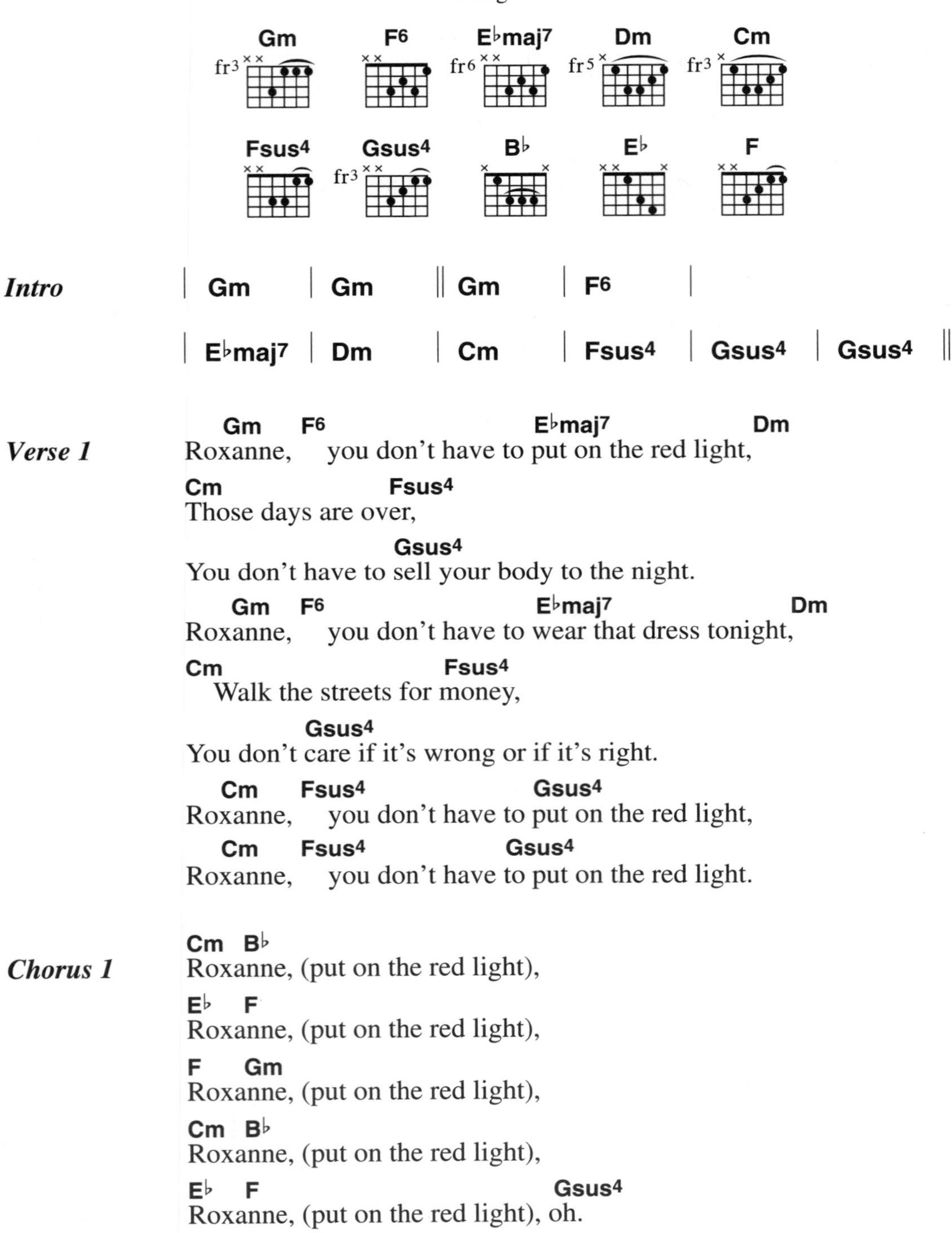

Intro

| Gm | Gm || Gm | F6 |

| E♭maj7 | Dm | Cm | Fsus4 | Gsus4 | Gsus4 ||

Verse 1

Gm F6 E♭maj7 Dm
Roxanne, you don't have to put on the red light,
Cm Fsus4
Those days are over,
Gsus4
You don't have to sell your body to the night.
Gm F6 E♭maj7 Dm
Roxanne, you don't have to wear that dress tonight,
Cm Fsus4
Walk the streets for money,
Gsus4
You don't care if it's wrong or if it's right.
Cm Fsus4 Gsus4
Roxanne, you don't have to put on the red light,
Cm Fsus4 Gsus4
Roxanne, you don't have to put on the red light.

Chorus 1

Cm B♭
Roxanne, (put on the red light),
E♭ F
Roxanne, (put on the red light),
F Gm
Roxanne, (put on the red light),
Cm B♭
Roxanne, (put on the red light),
E♭ F Gsus4
Roxanne, (put on the red light), oh.

Instrumental | Gm | Gm | Gm | Gm ||

Verse 2

```
 Gm                        F6
I loved you since I knew ya,
  E♭maj7                   Dm
I wouldn't talk down to ya,
 Cm                          Fsus4
I have to tell you just how I feel,
          Gsus4
I won't share you with another boy.
Gm                         F6
I know my mind is made up,
    E♭maj7                 Dm
So put away your make up,
Cm                      Fsus4
  Told you once, I won't tell you again,
       Gsus4
It's a crime the way...
     Cm     Fsus4                  Gsus4
Roxanne,     you don't have to put on the red light,
     Cm     Fsus4               Gsus4
Roxanne,     you don't have to put on the red light.
```

Chorus 2

```
   Cm   B♭
𝄆 Roxanne, (put on the red light),
E♭   F
Roxanne, (put on the red light),
F    Gm
Roxanne, (put on the red light),
Cm  B♭
Roxanne, (put on the red light).   𝄇   Repeat to fade
```

S.O.S.

Words & Music by
Benny Andersson, Björn Ulvaeus & Stig Anderson

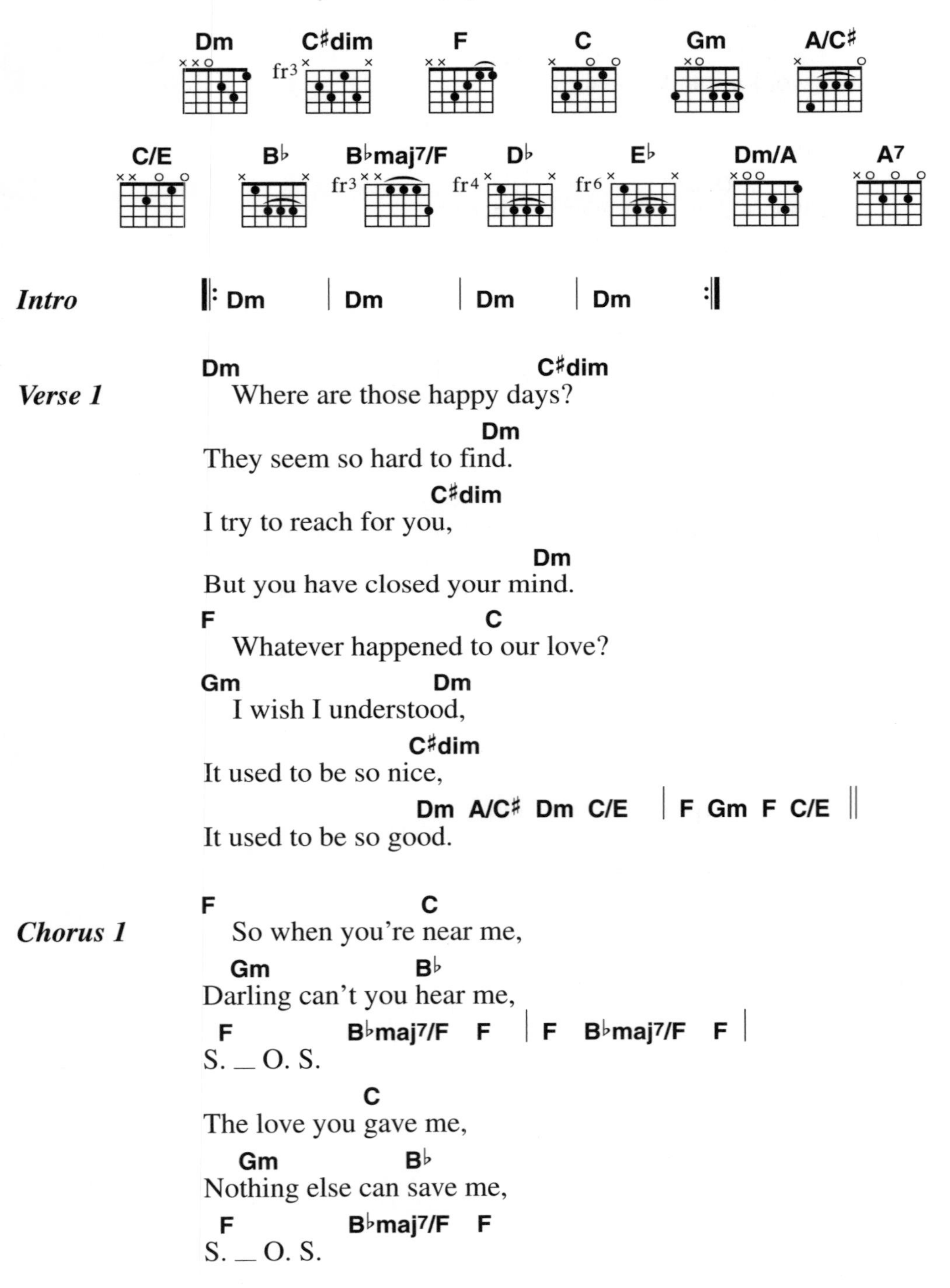

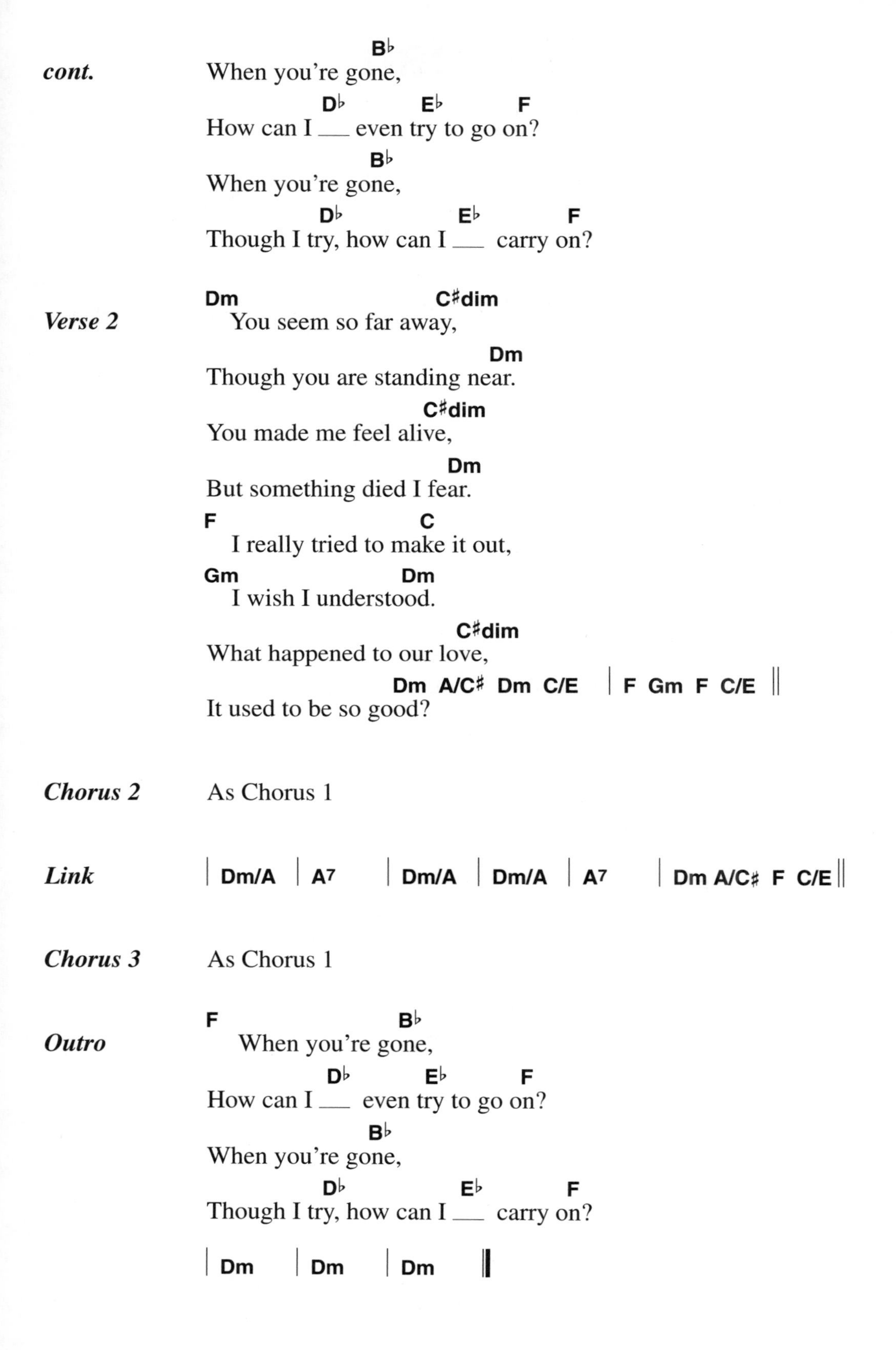

cont.

B♭
When you're gone,

D♭ E♭ F
How can I __ even try to go on?

B♭
When you're gone,

D♭ E♭ F
Though I try, how can I __ carry on?

Verse 2

Dm C♯dim
You seem so far away,

Dm
Though you are standing near.

C♯dim
You made me feel alive,

Dm
But something died I fear.

F C
I really tried to make it out,

Gm Dm
I wish I understood.

C♯dim
What happened to our love,

Dm A/C♯ Dm C/E | F Gm F C/E ||
It used to be so good?

Chorus 2

As Chorus 1

Link

| Dm/A | A7 | Dm/A | Dm/A | A7 | Dm A/C♯ F C/E ||

Chorus 3

As Chorus 1

Outro

F B♭
When you're gone,

D♭ E♭ F
How can I __ even try to go on?

B♭
When you're gone,

D♭ E♭ F
Though I try, how can I __ carry on?

| Dm | Dm | Dm ||

Starman

Words & Music by
David Bowie

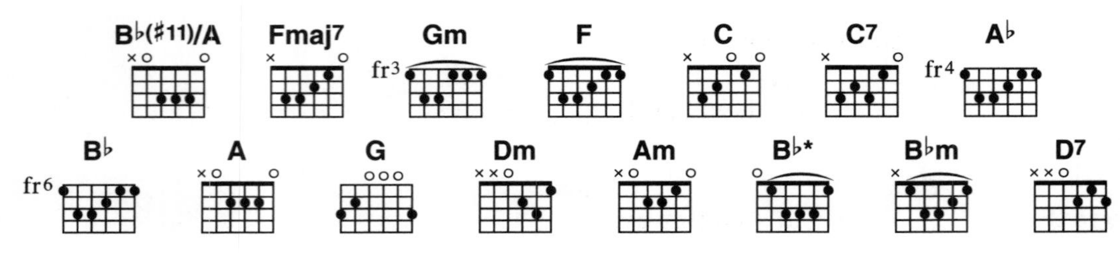

Intro 𝄆 B♭(♯11)/A | | Fmaj7 | 𝄇

Verse 1

Gm
Didn't know what time it was,

The lights were low-ow-ow.

F
I lean back on my radio-o-o,

C C7
Some cat was laying down some rock'n'roll,

F A♭ B♭
'Lotta soul', he said.

Verse 2

Gm
Then the loud sound did seem to fa-a-ade

F
Came back like a slow voice on a wave of pha-a-ase

C C7 A G
That weren't no D.J. that was hazy cosmic jive.

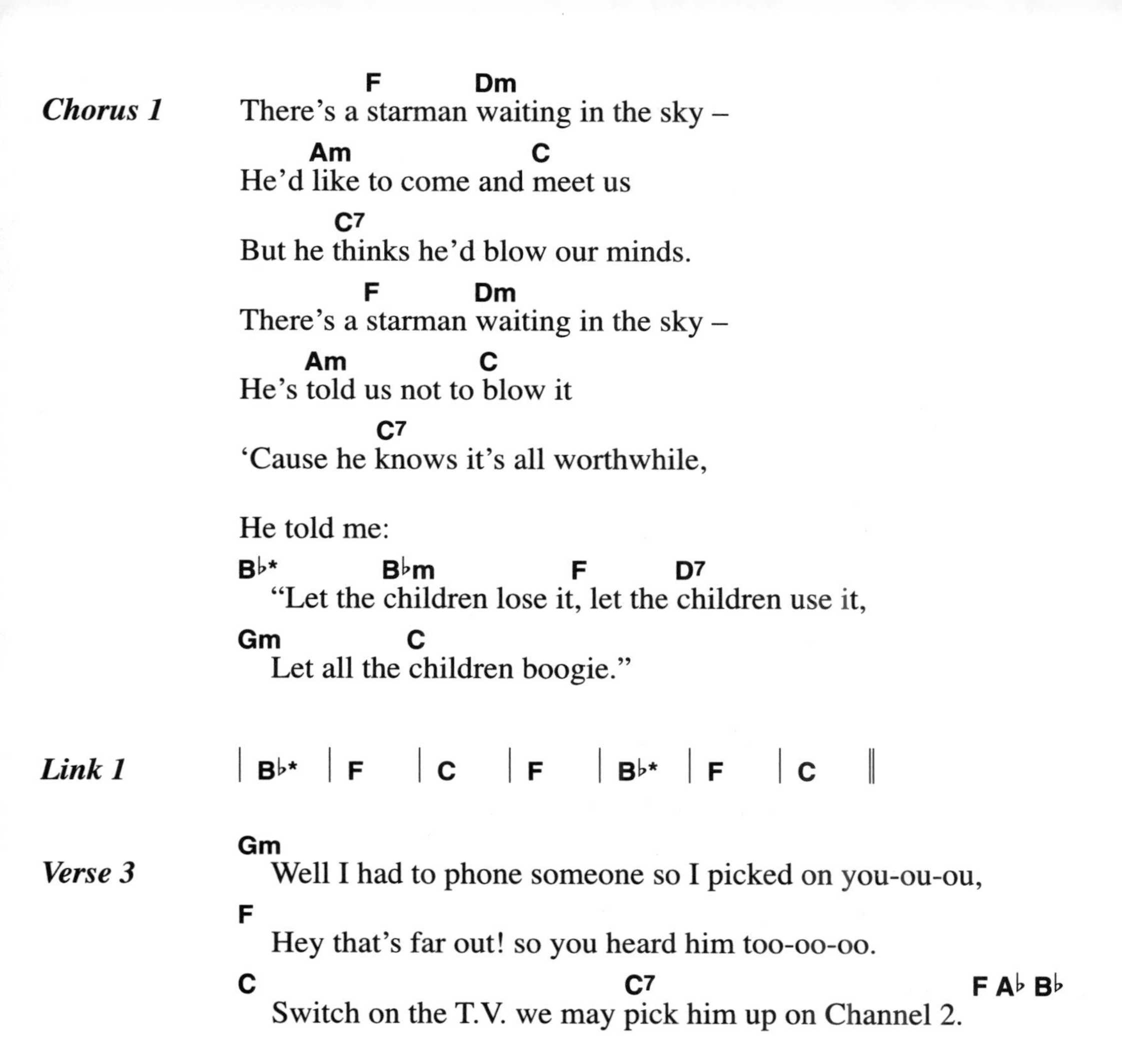

Chorus 1

F Dm
There's a starman waiting in the sky –
Am C
He'd like to come and meet us
C7
But he thinks he'd blow our minds.
F Dm
There's a starman waiting in the sky –
Am C
He's told us not to blow it
C7
'Cause he knows it's all worthwhile,

He told me:
B♭* B♭m F D7
"Let the children lose it, let the children use it,
Gm C
Let all the children boogie."

Link 1

| B♭* | F | C | F | B♭* | F | C ‖

Verse 3

Gm
Well I had to phone someone so I picked on you-ou-ou,
F
Hey that's far out! so you heard him too-oo-oo.
C C7 F A♭ B♭
Switch on the T.V. we may pick him up on Channel 2.

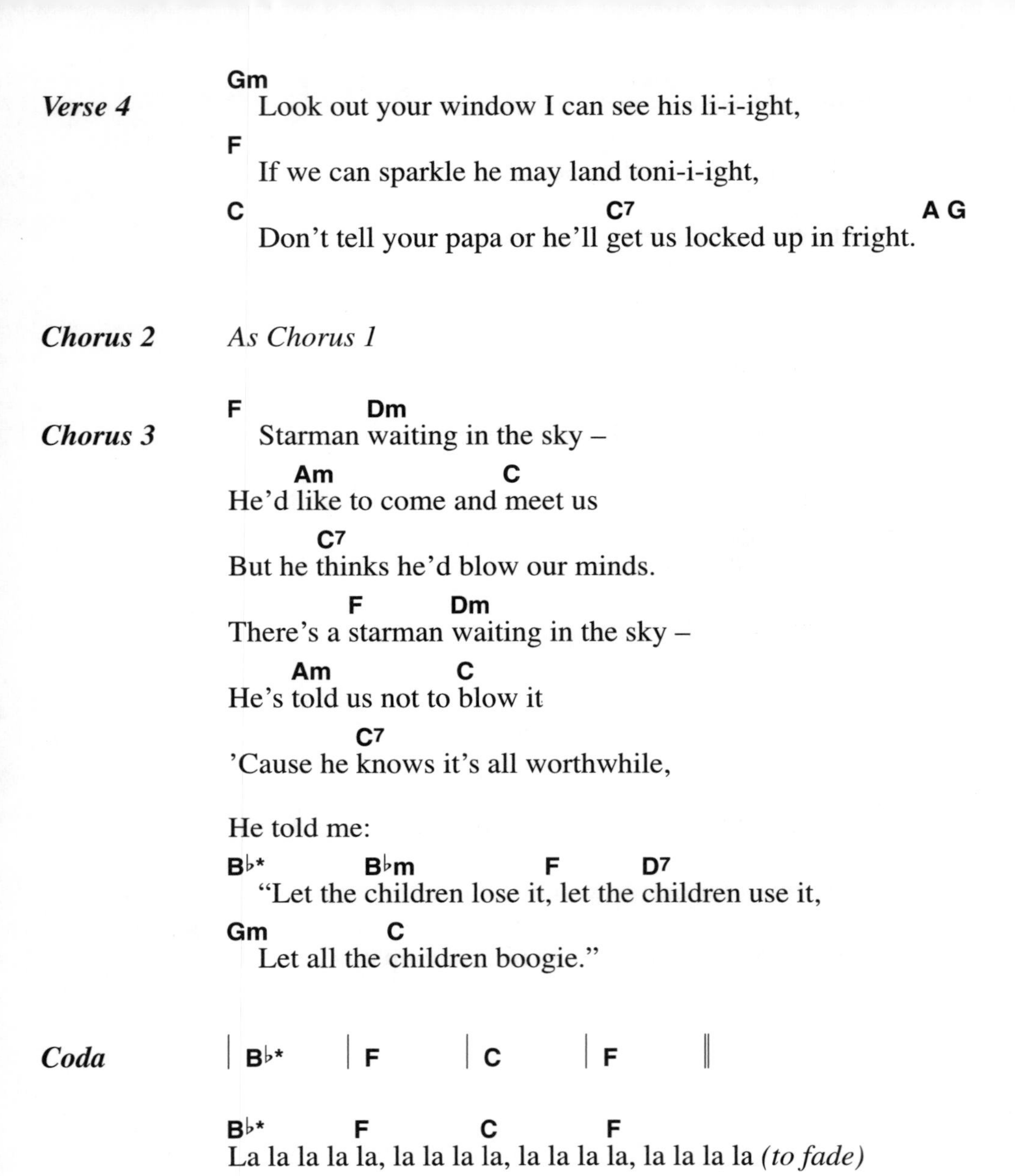

Verse 4

Gm
Look out your window I can see his li-i-ight,
F
If we can sparkle he may land toni-i-ight,
C   C7   A G
Don't tell your papa or he'll get us locked up in fright.

Chorus 2 — *As Chorus 1*

Chorus 3

F   Dm
Starman waiting in the sky –
Am   C
He'd like to come and meet us
C7
But he thinks he'd blow our minds.
F   Dm
There's a starman waiting in the sky –
Am   C
He's told us not to blow it
C7
'Cause he knows it's all worthwhile,

He told me:
B♭*   B♭m   F   D7
"Let the children lose it, let the children use it,
Gm   C
Let all the children boogie."

Coda

| B♭* | F | C | F ||

B♭*   F   C   F
La la la la la, la la la la, la la la la, la la la la *(to fade)*

Sultans Of Swing

Words & Music by
Mark Knopfler

Dm C B♭ A F

Intro | Dm | Dm | Dm | Dm :|

Verse 1

Dm C B♭ A
You get a shiver in the dark, it's a-rainin' in the park, but meantime
Dm C B♭ A
South of the river, you stop and you hold everything.
F C
A band is blowin' dixie, double four time,
B♭ Dm B♭ C
You feel alright when you hear that music ring.

Verse 2

Dm C B♭ A
Well now you step inside but you don't see too many faces
Dm C B♭ A
Comin' in out of the rain to hear the jazz go down.
F C
Competition in other places,
B♭ Dm B♭
Oh, but the horns, they're blowin' that sound.
C B♭
Way on down South,
C Dm C B♭ C
Way on down South in London town.

Link | Dm C | B♭ | C | C ||

Verse 3

Dm C B♭ A
You check out Guitar George, he knows all the chords,
Dm C B♭ A
Mind he's strictly rhythm, he doesn't want to make it cry or sing.
F C
Yes, and an old guitar is all he can afford
B♭ Dm B♭ C
When he gets up under the lights to play his thing.

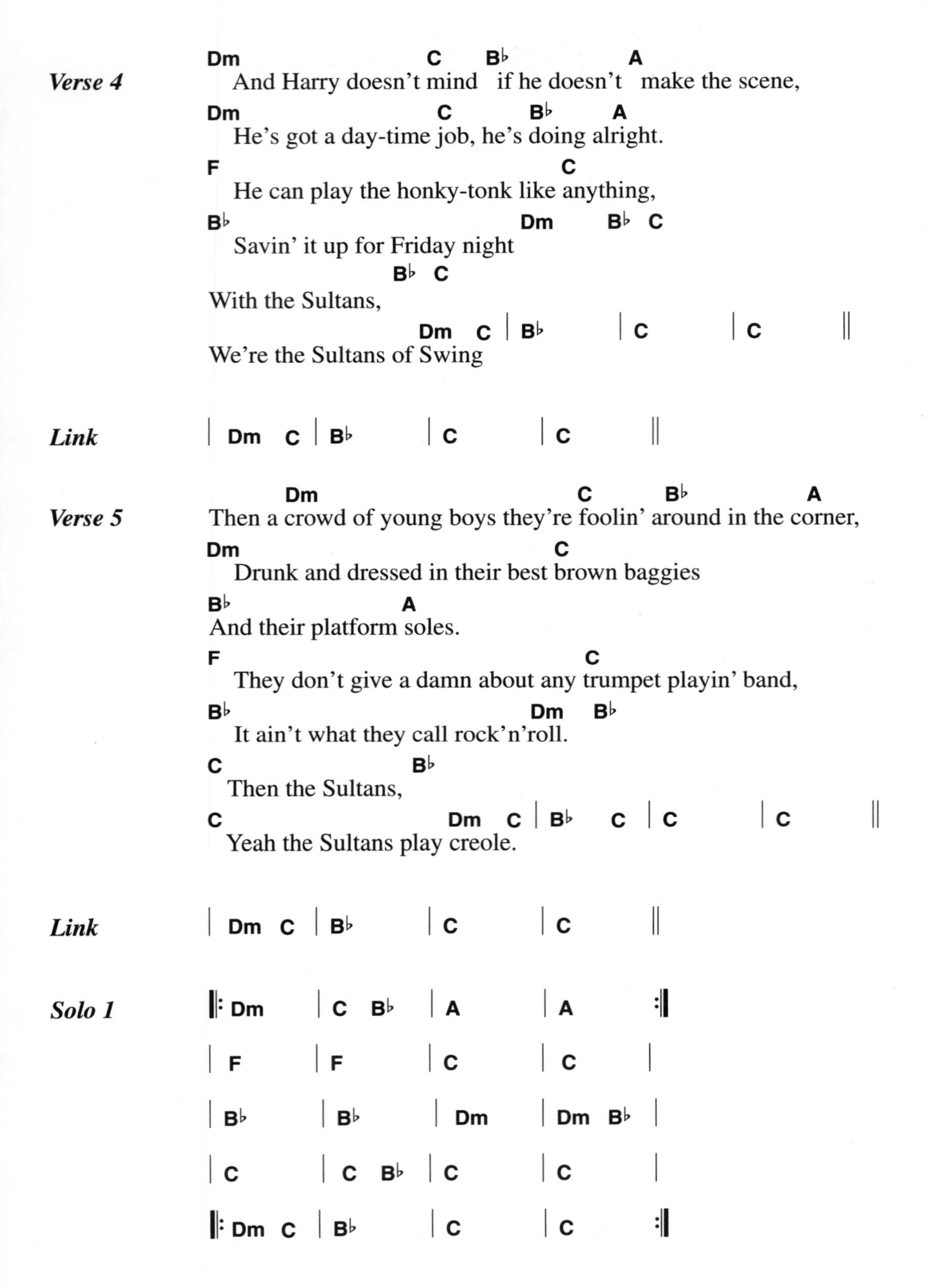
Verse 4
Dm C B♭ A
And Harry doesn't mind if he doesn't make the scene,
Dm C B♭ A
He's got a day-time job, he's doing alright.
F C
He can play the honky-tonk like anything,
B♭ Dm B♭ C
Savin' it up for Friday night
B♭ C
With the Sultans,
Dm C | B♭ | C | C ||
We're the Sultans of Swing
Link
| Dm C | B♭ | C | C ||
Verse 5
Dm C B♭ A
Then a crowd of young boys they're foolin' around in the corner,
Dm C
Drunk and dressed in their best brown baggies
B♭ A
And their platform soles.
F C
They don't give a damn about any trumpet playin' band,
B♭ Dm B♭
It ain't what they call rock'n'roll.
C B♭
Then the Sultans,
C Dm C | B♭ C | C | C ||
Yeah the Sultans play creole.
Link
| Dm C | B♭ | C | C ||
Solo 1
: Dm	C B♭	A	A :
F	F	C	C
B♭	B♭	Dm	Dm B♭
C	C B♭	C	C
: Dm C	B♭	C	C :

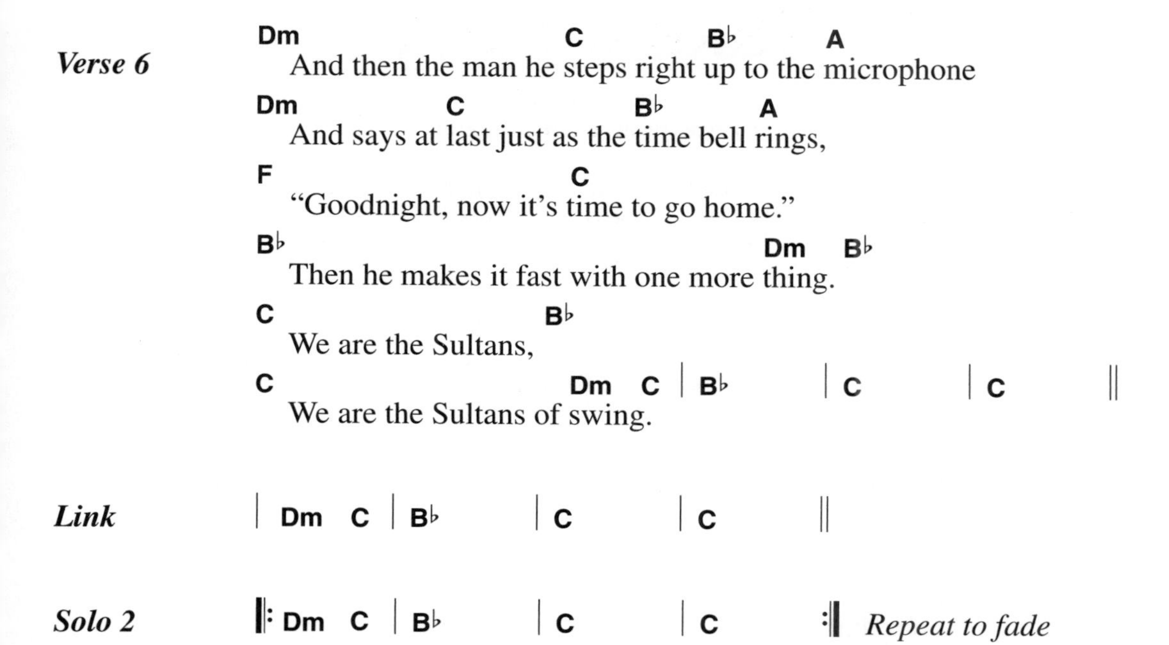
Verse 6
Dm C B♭ A
And then the man he steps right up to the microphone
Dm C B♭ A
And says at last just as the time bell rings,
F C
"Goodnight, now it's time to go home."
B♭ Dm B♭
Then he makes it fast with one more thing.
C B♭
We are the Sultans,
C Dm C | B♭ | C | C ||
We are the Sultans of swing.
Link
| Dm C | B♭ | C | C ||
Solo 2
||: Dm C | B♭ | C | C :|| Repeat to fade

Take It Easy

Words & Music by
Jackson Browne & Glenn Frey

G C D7sus4 D Em Am G7

Tune guitar slightly flat

Intro |: G | G | C | D7sus4 :| G | G ||

Verse 1

```
               G
Well I'm a-runnin' down the road tryin' to loosen my load,
                          D       C
I've got seven women on my mind.
G                         D
Four that wanna own me, two that wanna stone me,
  C                      G
One says she's a friend of mine.
```

Chorus 1

```
         Em          C   G
Take it easy, take it ea - sy,
              Am                 C                 Em
Don't let the sound of your own wheels drive you crazy.
        C              G              C            G
Lighten up while you still can, don't even try to understand,
          Am                   C              G
Just find a place to make your stand and take it easy.

| G      | G      ||
```

Verse 2

```
               G
Well I'm a-standin' on a corner in Winslow, Arizona,
                    D       C
And such a fine sight to see;
          G           D
It's a girl, my Lord, in a flat-bed Ford,
        C                  G
Slowin' down to take a look at me.
```

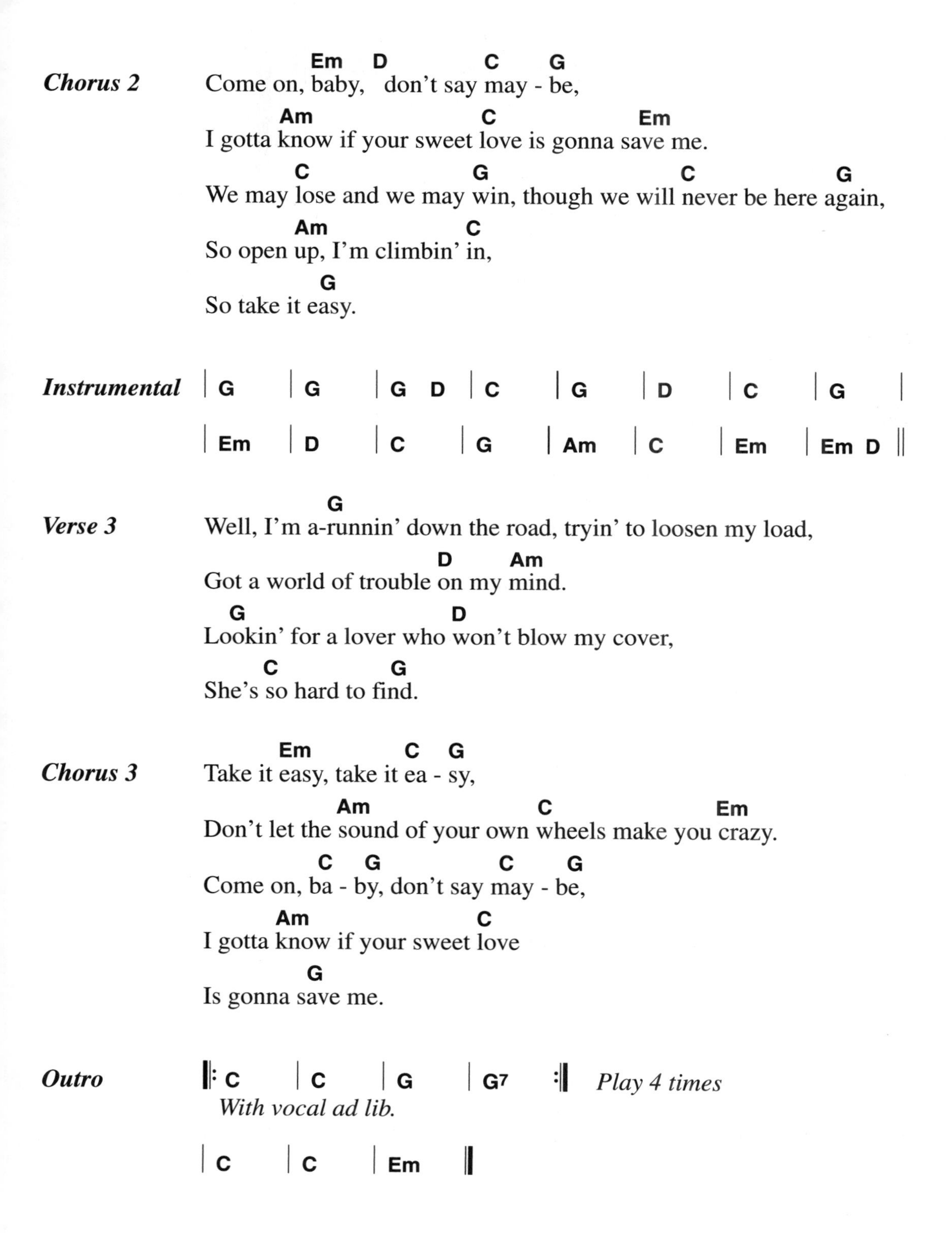

Chorus 2

Em D C G
Come on, baby, don't say may - be,

Am C Em
I gotta know if your sweet love is gonna save me.

C G C G
We may lose and we may win, though we will never be here again,

Am C
So open up, I'm climbin' in,

G
So take it easy.

Instrumental

| G | G | G D | C | G | D | C | G |

| Em | D | C | G | Am | C | Em | Em D ||

Verse 3

G
Well, I'm a-runnin' down the road, tryin' to loosen my load,

D Am
Got a world of trouble on my mind.

G D
Lookin' for a lover who won't blow my cover,

C G
She's so hard to find.

Chorus 3

Em C G
Take it easy, take it ea - sy,

Am C Em
Don't let the sound of your own wheels make you crazy.

C G C G
Come on, ba - by, don't say may - be,

Am C
I gotta know if your sweet love

G
Is gonna save me.

Outro

|: C | C | G | G7 :| *Play 4 times*
With vocal ad lib.

| C | C | Em ||

Virginia Plain

Words & Music by
Bryan Ferry

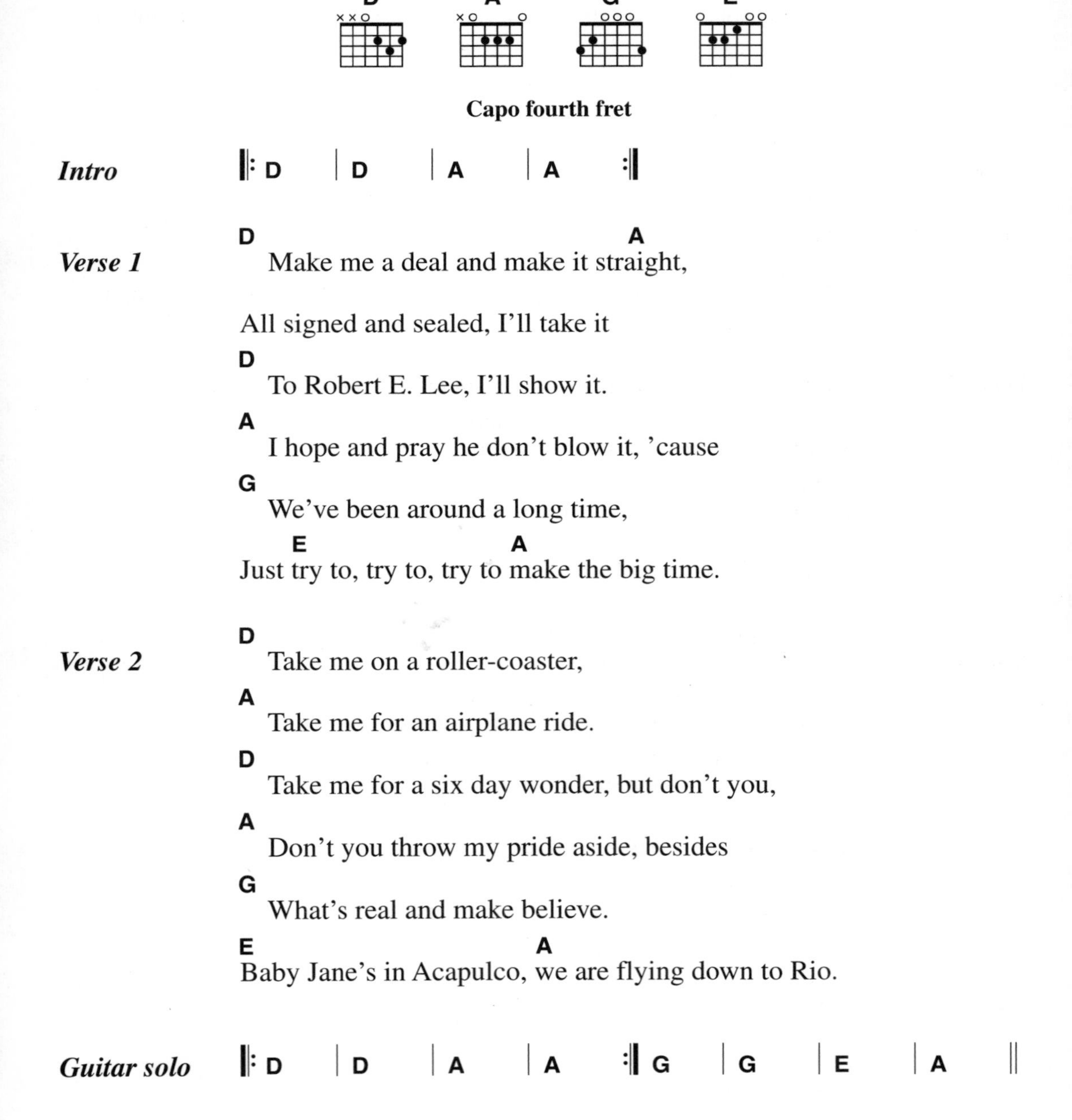

Capo fourth fret

Intro ‖: D | D | A | A :‖

Verse 1

```
D                                       A
   Make me a deal and make it straight,
All signed and sealed, I'll take it
D
   To Robert E. Lee, I'll show it.
A
   I hope and pray he don't blow it, 'cause
G
   We've been around a long time,
     E                      A
Just try to, try to, try to make the big time.
```

Verse 2

```
D
   Take me on a roller-coaster,
A
   Take me for an airplane ride.
D
   Take me for a six day wonder, but don't you,
A
   Don't you throw my pride aside, besides
G
   What's real and make believe.
E                             A
Baby Jane's in Acapulco, we are flying down to Rio.
```

Guitar solo ‖: D | D | A | A :‖ G | G | E | A ‖

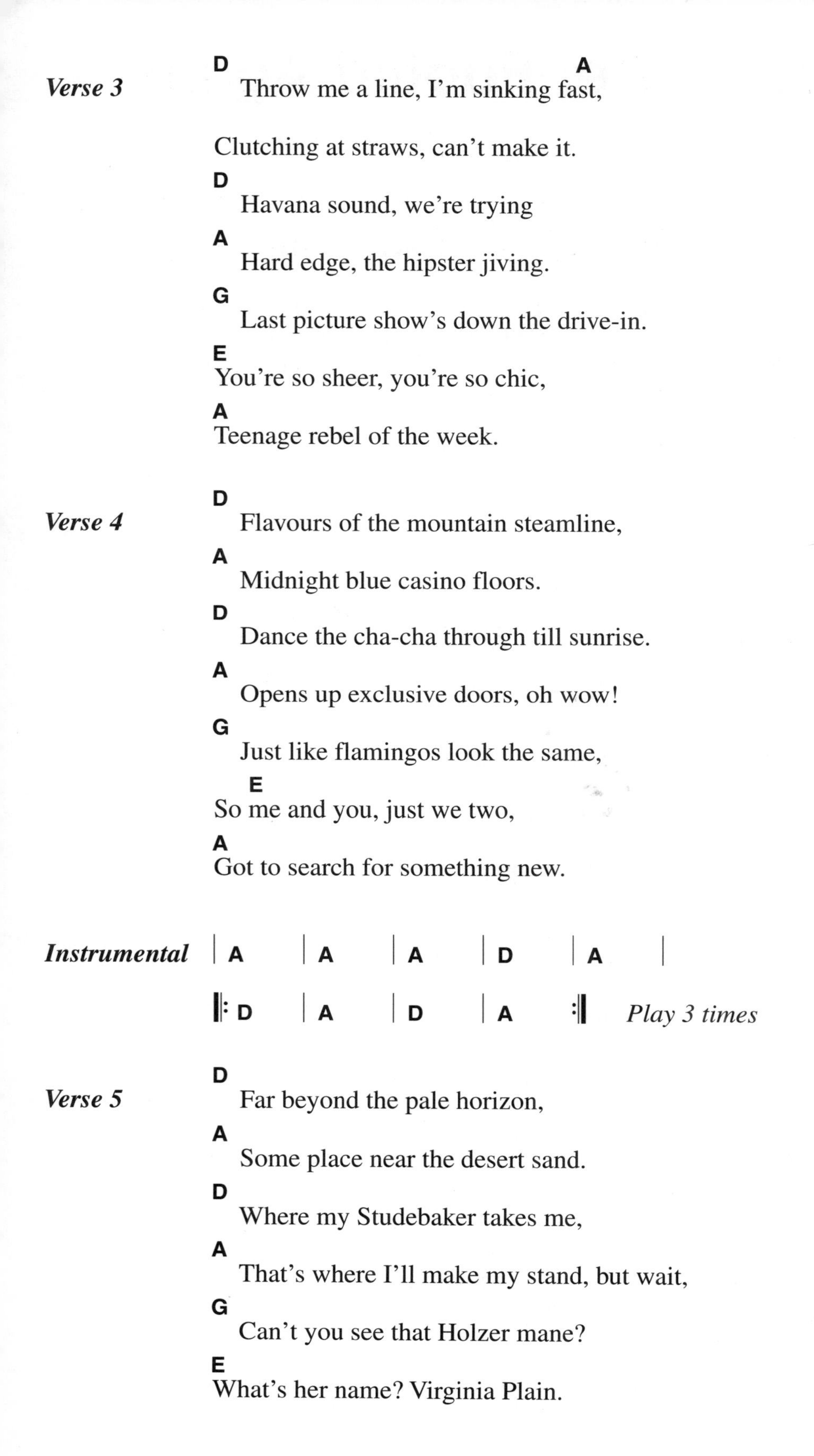

Verse 3

D   A
Throw me a line, I'm sinking fast,

Clutching at straws, can't make it.

D
Havana sound, we're trying

A
Hard edge, the hipster jiving.

G
Last picture show's down the drive-in.

E
You're so sheer, you're so chic,

A
Teenage rebel of the week.

Verse 4

D
Flavours of the mountain steamline,

A
Midnight blue casino floors.

D
Dance the cha-cha through till sunrise.

A
Opens up exclusive doors, oh wow!

G
Just like flamingos look the same,

E
So me and you, just we two,

A
Got to search for something new.

Instrumental | A | A | A | D | A |

|: D | A | D | A :| *Play 3 times*

Verse 5

D
Far beyond the pale horizon,

A
Some place near the desert sand.

D
Where my Studebaker takes me,

A
That's where I'll make my stand, but wait,

G
Can't you see that Holzer mane?

E
What's her name? Virginia Plain.

Won't Get Fooled Again

Words & Music by
Pete Townshend

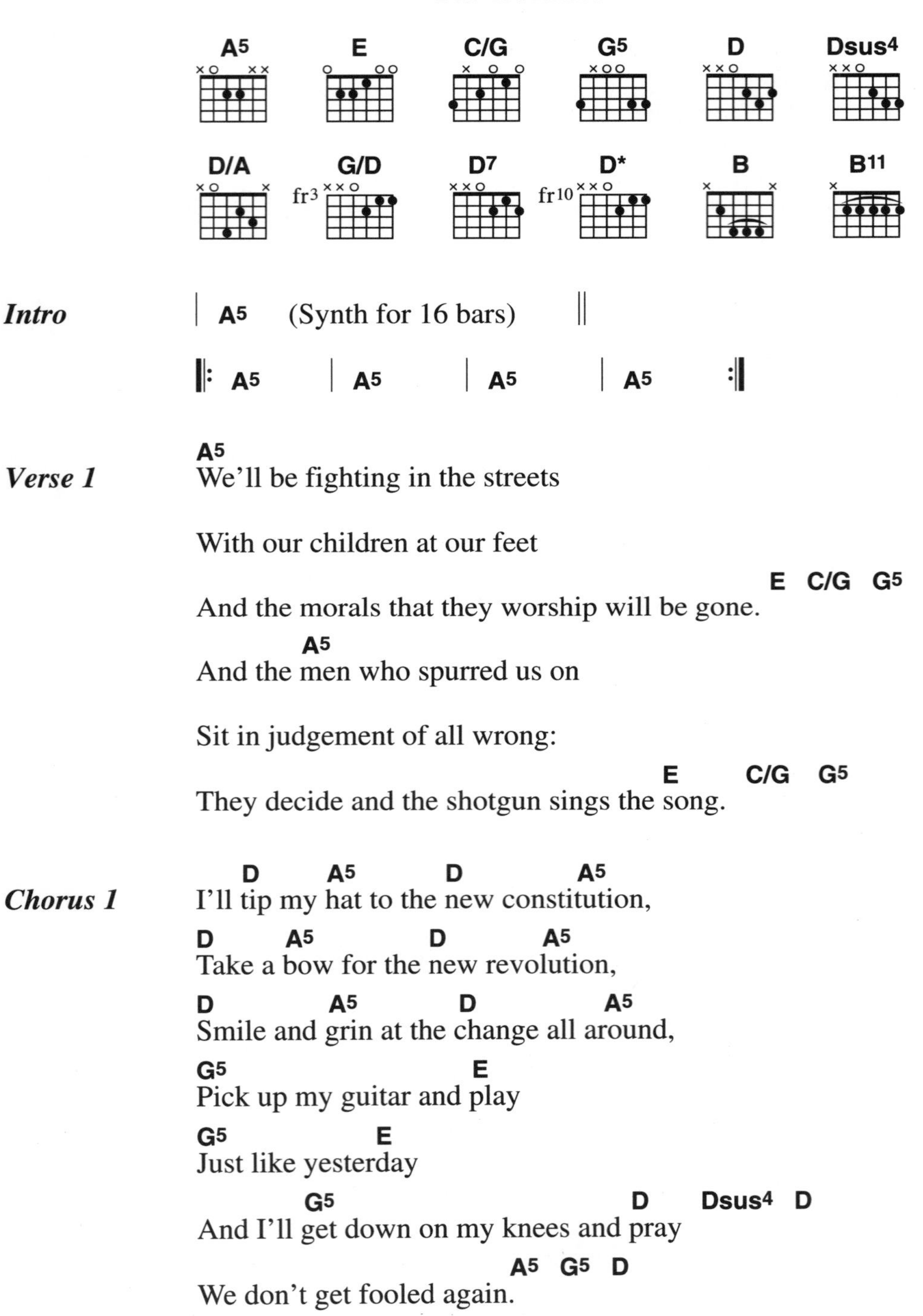

Intro

| A5 (Synth for 16 bars) ||

|: A5 | A5 | A5 | A5 :|

Verse 1

```
A5
We'll be fighting in the streets

With our children at our feet
                                                 E  C/G  G5
And the morals that they worship will be gone.
          A5
And the men who spurred us on

Sit in judgement of all wrong:
                                         E      C/G   G5
They decide and the shotgun sings the song.
```

Chorus 1

```
    D     A5       D        A5
I'll tip my hat to the new constitution,
D     A5      D      A5
Take a bow for the new revolution,
D        A5       D        A5
Smile and grin at the change all around,
G5                E
Pick up my guitar and play
G5           E
Just like yesterday
        G5                    D   Dsus4  D
And I'll get down on my knees and pray
                          A5 G5 D
We don't get fooled again.
```

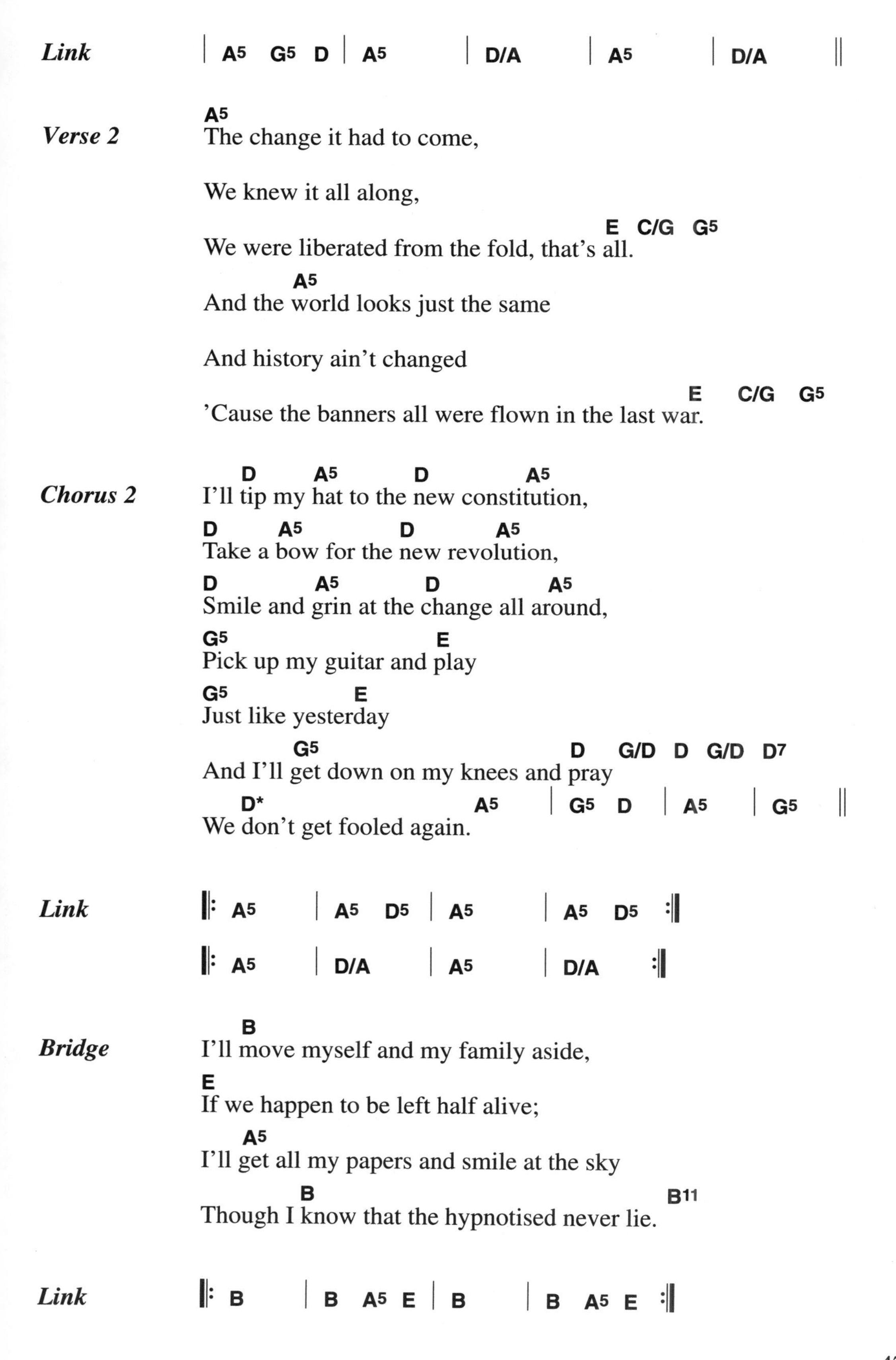

Link | A5 G5 D | A5 | D/A | A5 | D/A ||

Verse 2

A5
The change it had to come,

We knew it all along,

E C/G G5
We were liberated from the fold, that's all.

A5
And the world looks just the same

And history ain't changed

E C/G G5
'Cause the banners all were flown in the last war.

Chorus 2

D A5 D A5
I'll tip my hat to the new constitution,

D A5 D A5
Take a bow for the new revolution,

D A5 D A5
Smile and grin at the change all around,

G5 E
Pick up my guitar and play

G5 E
Just like yesterday

G5 D G/D D G/D D7
And I'll get down on my knees and pray

D* A5 | G5 D | A5 | G5 ||
We don't get fooled again.

Link

|: A5 | A5 D5 | A5 | A5 D5 :|

|: A5 | D/A | A5 | D/A :|

Bridge

B
I'll move myself and my family aside,

E
If we happen to be left half alive;

A5
I'll get all my papers and smile at the sky

B B11
Though I know that the hypnotised never lie.

Link |: B | B A5 E | B | B A5 E :|

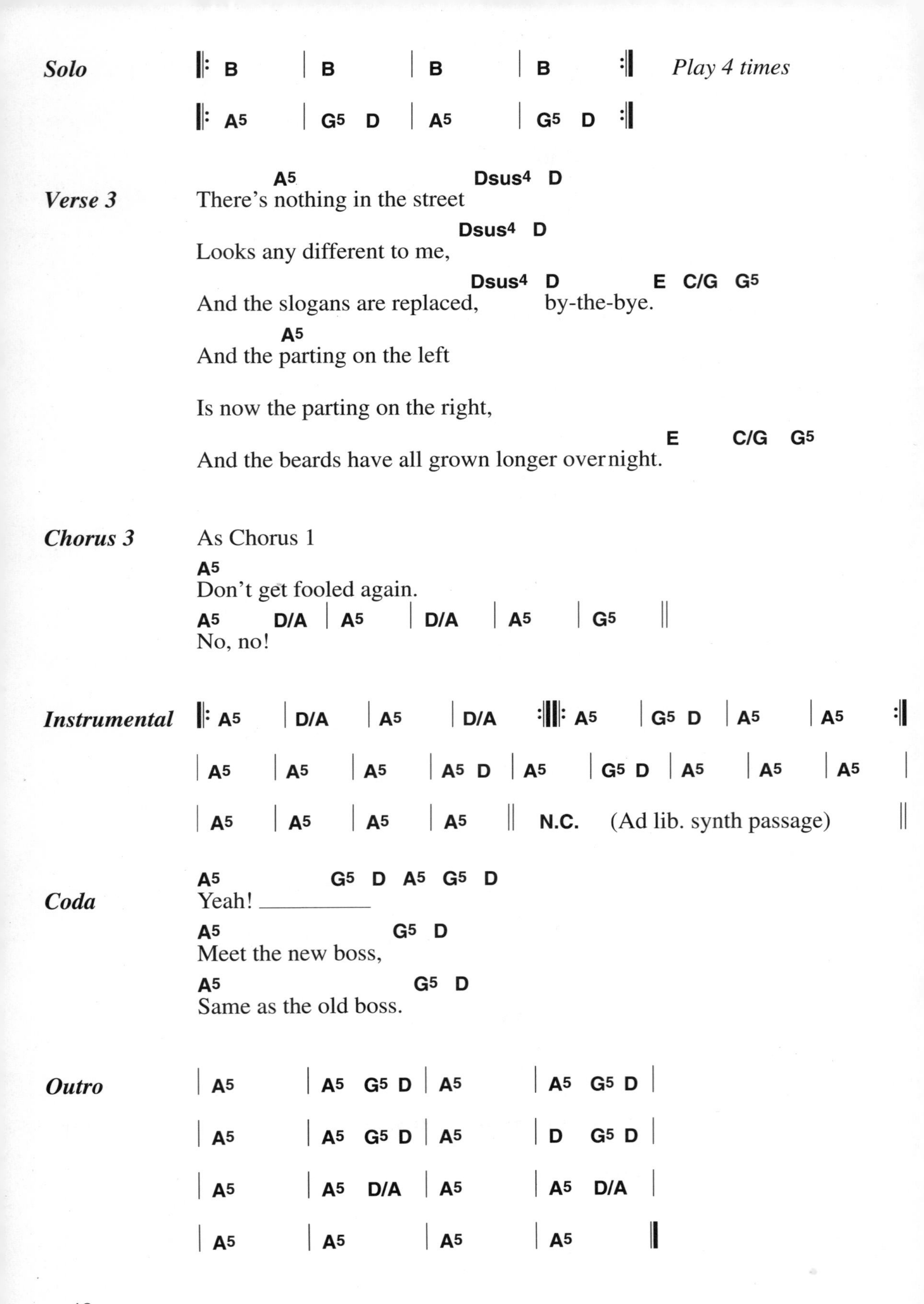
Solo
|: B | B | B | B :| Play 4 times
|: A5 | G5 D | A5 | G5 D :|
Verse 3
A5 Dsus4 D
There's nothing in the street
Dsus4 D
Looks any different to me,
Dsus4 D E C/G G5
And the slogans are replaced, by-the-bye.
A5
And the parting on the left
Is now the parting on the right,
E C/G G5
And the beards have all grown longer overnight.
Chorus 3
As Chorus 1
A5
Don't get fooled again.
A5 D/A | A5 | D/A | A5 | G5 ||
No, no!
Instrumental
: A5	D/A	A5	D/A :		: A5	G5 D	A5	A5 :
A5	A5	A5	A5 D	A5	G5 D	A5	A5	A5
A5	A5	A5	A5		N.C. (Ad lib. synth passage)	
Coda
A5 G5 D A5 G5 D
Yeah! ________
A5 G5 D
Meet the new boss,
A5 G5 D
Same as the old boss.
Outro
A5	A5 G5 D	A5	A5 G5 D
A5	A5 G5 D	A5	D G5 D
A5	A5 D/A	A5	A5 D/A
A5	A5	A5	A5	